As readers of Joyce Stranger's earlier books will know, the author arouses equal interest in both human and animal characters. She is a trained scientist, writing without sentimentality and with strict adherence to fact, with a deep feeling for wild animals and tame, and for people who are involved with them.

A DOG CALLED GELERT AND OTHER STORIES is about dogs – all kinds of dogs, wild, tame, happy, bad and obedient – and their masters, and of the special relationships that often develop between dog and owner. It is at once tender, moving, sharply observant and informative – and a worthy successor to her last impressive novel, *Chia, The Wildcat*.

Also by Joyce Stranger

and published by Corgi Books

Joyce Stranger

A Dog Called Gelert
and other stories

CORGI BOOKS

A DOG CALLED GELERT

A CORGI BOOK 0 552 09399 8

First publication in Great Britain

PRINTING HISTORY
Corgi edition published 1973
Corgi edition reprinted 1975
Corgi edition reprinted 1976
Corgi edition reprinted 1978
Corgi edition reissued 1983

This book is set in Monotype Baskerville

Corgi Books are published by Transworld Publishers Ltd.,
Century House, 61-63 Uxbridge Road,
Ealing, London W5 5SA.
Made and printed in Great Britain by
Hunt Barnard Printing Ltd., Aylesbury, Bucks.

To my mother- and father-in-law
With love

Contents

Chapter 1

Barrie Evans hated home and he hated school.

He did not hate his parents. They were also trapped. Da and Mam were kind enough and reasonable in most things, but ever since he was five years old they had lived seven floors up in a fifteen storey block of flats in the middle of a town, and Barrie could not understand why. Barrie did not hate the flats. He loathed them with all his heart.

He loathed having people round him, so close. People next door, on either side, people above, and people below. People who talked and laughed and shouted, who blared the telly half the day and all of the evening; people who had rough children who mocked at Barrie and laughed at his strange accent and nicknamed him Taffy and Foureyes, because of his spectacles. He hated them more every day.

He had been born in Wales, in a little valley set among the mountains. Here his parents owned a tiny farm. A few cows, some mountain sheep that grazed on the high hills under the lonely sky; a few chickens, and the dogs.

From his little room under the eaves, where the ceiling sloped to the window and the birds nested above him, friendly under the tiles, chattering to him in the morning, tiny feet scratching, he could see the stern sweep of Tryfan and the twin tops of the Rivals. Below them were the patchwork fields and the wide horizons and beyond them was the sea. They had no neighbours for almost a mile. Daily Barrie trotted to the end of the valley and took the newspaper and the few letters from the drainpipe under the hedge. There was no danger from cars. Only the rare Land Rover came up the steep track. There were no other children. No one to mock and torment and tease him. Only himself, and Mam and Da, and the animals on the farm. He had the wide moors to rove on, where the sparrowhawk soared above him and the kestrel hovered, and the mountain hare bounded along and turned to watch him, ears listening for the sound of danger. One crack from the quarry over the mountain and she was away, loping through the heather.

There were two dogs to play with, and they were better than any companions that Barrie could imagine. Or rather, there was a dog and a bitch. Bob and Meg. When Meg had no puppies, and was not herding the sheep, she helped Bob herd Barrie. They guarded him from falling in the deep stream that ran and chuckled its way over the clean grey boulders. Barrie knew the stream well, knew where, when it had not rained for long enough, he could paddle without harm; knew where the trout lay in the deep pools and hid under the overhang; knew where he could safely swim. But all the time the herd dogs guarded him. They prevented him from being lost on the mountains. They barked at the summer strangers who sometimes hiked over the hills and came to the farm for a glass of fresh milk, warm from the nanny goat Mirabel, and who spoke in strange accents that were difficult for Barrie to understand. He still found it easier to speak in Welsh and he and Mam often talked their own language together, but Da insisted he must learn English too as he had to go to school and he needed it to get on in the world.

Barrie wondered about the world. His world was the farmhouse where the kitchen was always warm winter and summer, warm from the big stove that heated the water and cooked the food and had to be fed day and night.

"There's greedy it is," Mam would say, exasperated, when it had swallowed all the wood he could find on the hillside and a load of coke besides. "The awful old thing."

For all that, the food that Mam cooked and the bread she baked was without equal and it was good to come in out of the wintry cold, and smell the warm breadsmell that was like a song in the kitchen and was part of Mam so that it clung to her clothes and Barrie buried his nose in her and sniffed her like a puppy and his father laughed.

"There's a little dog we have, another puppy and not a boy at all," he would tease, and Barrie would laugh at his Da, such a big man, standing tall on those strong legs of his, his red face a-grin with delight, his thick body smelling of sheep and dogs and the goats that he had milked each morning and evening, and smelling too of safety and comfort, able to soothe a small boy who had fallen and cut his knee, or heard the wicked mountain devils thundering above Tryfan and scything the sky with their frightening forked light.

Life was fun, most of the time. There were lambs in spring, racing over the fields, turning to face him and leap away again, running to their mothers and burying their faces in the warm fleece, as anxious for comfort as he was when his tummy ached and he called for Mam in the dark and owl-full night. There were the summer calves, and Mirabel's chunky white kids who loved to run and jump and butt with a small boy, so that he had endless games with them. There were the soft Easter chicks, running wild in the yard, small and fluffy and yellow, with matchstick legs and indiarubber beaks and tiny bright pebbledark eyes that glittered at him. There were ducks that came when he called, and thrust their beaks into the bucket of food, and sometimes were so bold that they flew into the bucket and dived hungrily in the corn so that he had to put it down on the ground as he could not hold it against such an invasion.

There were trees to climb, sparse and stunted and twisted with the wind that Tryfan threw at them, but trees for all that with bendy branches and leaves that grew thick in summer and fell in the autumn gales and drifted into the house and that he ran to catch. Catch a falling leaf for luck. Mam knew all the old stories, the story of the lady who came from the lake with her herds of cattle, and married the Prince and lived with him happily until one day, in anger, he struck her and she returned to the water, she and all the cows and all the calves they had borne in the years she had spent with him, and she wept as she entered the water. And when the wind sobbed in the chimney and whipped the foam from the lake and the rain lashed at the windows Mam would say, "Ah, indeed it is the Prince sorrowing for his lady and she has left him alone so many years. I wonder, will she ever come again?" So that when Barrie passed the lake, he looked at the water, half in fear and half in hope, thinking he might see her come out of the drowned deep, come with her long fair seaweed hair and her loveliness that was more, Da said, than ever mortal woman's, come with her following herds, and walk up the hillside and meet her Prince. But she never came.

And then, when Barrie was five years and two months and one week old, all this ended. He was feeding the chickens and had paused to scratch the back of the old black pig who loved having his hide rubbed and who, when Barrie passed by and put his tow head over the sty door and grunted at him, grunted companionably back. It was fun to see who made the loudest grunts. Old Black nearly always won.

That day, Da came home from the market town with a face on him blacker than the thunderheads that brooded over Tryfan. He never looked at Barrie, never stopped to scratch the pig, never glanced at Mirabel's little new kid, but walked on, his heavy boots tramping over the cobbles, into the kitchen, and slammed the door with a noise that echoed back from the mountains, and frightened Barrie who had never known Da do anything like that before. Later, he crept into the kitchen for tea, but Mam had forgotten to make the tea and was sitting in the big chair, rocking herself to and fro, the angry cat clutched tight against her while she cried more tears than there ever was water in the Elwyn brook.

After that, nothing was the same again. Men came to the farm. Men in shiny boots. Men with thick legs and weathered faces and rough tongues. Men who strode in and out of the farmyard and made rude remarks about the sheep and the goats. Men who stuck labels on all the farm implements; on the big tractor that Da had named Jezebel. Because she was as wicked as the evil queen and once had thrown him and trapped his leg and Mam had had to drive to the next farm and they came home and lifted Jezebel off Da and he was in bed for two weeks and the men from the next farm did his work for him. They were always neighbourly in the valley and a man would walk ten miles to help a stranger if he were in trouble.

These men were not like that. They had no time for small boys and Barrie learned to go away before he was sent away, and watch from a distance. He had decided the world was about to end and that Tryfan would fall on them all and they had to go away from the farm, but he did not know where. He had never been further than Bangor in all of his life and Bangor was enormous, so great a city with all those people and all those houses and the brightly lit shops. He had been taken there at Christmas, and gone to the Cathedral and listened to the angels singing, Da said. The angels looked like ordinary boys and ordinary ladies, but the singing was something to remember all of his life. He tried to remember it now, because it was frightening to see Da like the black clouds with no smile and no light in his eyes and Mam so unhappy that she only had to look at you and she cried.

"Oh, Barrie, boy bach, what in the world will become of us?" she'd ask as she grabbed him tight and held him against her as if crushing the breath from his body would present Tryfan from falling. No one had said it was going to fall, but old Mrs. Mair Pritchard at the other end of the valley was always saying that something would not happen till Tryfan fell on all of us, and there was nothing else that could account for such misery on his parents' part. At night he looked up at Tryfan, Tryfan that was a demon mountain and hard to climb, harder perhaps than any other, and that claimed at least one human victim every year. One young man had come to their farmhouse for milk and the very next day the Mountain Rescue came looking and found him on the hillside and took him to the Infirmary.

Yet whenever he looked up Tryfan was still standing, as wild and uncompromising as ever. But five times as terrifying.

Then came the day that was more frightening than all the others. Tractors and Land Rovers drove up to the door, and farmers from all over Wales came inside, and walked through the rooms, and looked at the stock. Gwyn Williams from the little farm at the far end of the valley beyond Tryfan towered over Barrie and patted him on his tow head and said most mysteriously,

"There, boy bach, there's lucky you are. You'll be going to a much bigger place soon, with other children to come and play. You'll learn to be a professor, or maybe a lawyer, or perhaps a judge. There's lucky you are to be going into the big city. He'll learn to be a man now, won't he, Megan Evans?"

His mother nodded. She had no more tears, and stared dry-eyed, watching her home vanish around her. Her lips still trembled and his father was curtly gruff and his mouth was a fierce red straight slash in his face and there were no smiles in his grey eyes. They were as dark and cold as the mountain stream when the ice bit deep in winter.

His mother made coffee and made sandwiches and the voices flowed over Barrie's head, saying words that meant nothing to him then but that meant much more later. His mother and father had gone outside to show some of the other men the stock, all rounded up and penned, and the dogs both kennelled, and those who stayed had forgotten Barrie, sitting on his small stool in a corner, listening, trying to make sense of all that was happening.

"Morgan Evans is a good man. It is a shame it has to come to this," said one farmer, a small and wizened old man in a green check coat that was several sizes too big for him and hung in folds around his diminished body.

"It is nobody's fault. Three bad winters in a row killed the lambs for all of us. Morgan is higher up the valley than we are. It was worse for him."

"It is a pity the bank could not wait for the money. The farm could recover," said a big man whose voice echoed in the small room and who made everyone else look small too.

"There is no time, Huw Griffiths," Barrie's Da said, coming back into the room. "It is no use talking. I have thought it over well, believe me. Also if we leave the valley, the boy can go to a really good school. It is lonely here for him."

Why is it lonely, Barrie wondered. He was never lonely. There was so much to do and so much to see and always a lamb to be fed or a kid to run with or a calf needing a bucket of milk or Old Black to have his back scratched and play at grunting.

He watched and listened and then stared in disbelief as after the coffee was drunk and the sandwiches eaten a man got up on the platform where the churns stood ready for Da to put them on the tractor and talked away their animals, one by one. And when he had done, men took away the cows and his pig and all the chickens, and they were taking Gwyn the little new white bull calf, and they were even taking Meg and Bob and the old cat, and Meg and Bob were whining and tugging at their leashes, trying to get to Da and Da's face was so terrifying that Barrie fled into the kitchen and beat his fists against Mam's warm body and howled.

"There, there, boy bach," Mam said, but there were tears hot on his hand and they were not his tears.

That night the farm was silent except for the owl hoots that were long wailing notes of misery. No cock flew fussily at the hens. No calves lowed. No dog barked. In the morning Mam's eyes were red and swollen and Da couldn't say a civil word and shouted at Barrie when he dropped his mug at breakfast, and there was not a creature anywhere, nothing living, nothing warm, nothing running or breathing or calling to welcome the sun. And the sun shone and the valley was bright and the trees were green and the river glittered with light.

Da humped the furniture on to the tractor trailer and down the lane and Barrie stared in disbelief. Everything came out of the house, beds and tables and chairs, pans and blankets and clothes. It took a long time, as the trailer was very small, and there was a huge van at the end of the lane that swallowed up everything they owned. There was nothing left.

Nothing but the empty house and the marks on the walls where the furniture had been, and the shapes of the pictures and the notch by the door that showed how he had grown since he was very small, much too small to see over the top of the big dining room table.

They got into Da's old car and drove all day. Barrie was terrified by the number of cars on the road, by the immense lorries that hurtled towards them, by the noise and the roar and the din. He hated the smell of traffic and he felt sick. He tucked himself up against Mam, and tried to sleep. Mam would only say they were going to a new home and everything would be lovely, but she didn't say it as if she believed it and Barrie didn't want a new home.

He wanted to stay in his little room and look up at Tryfan. And to watch the sparrowhawk and play with the lambs and swim in the river pool, and fish with Da beside him, even though he never caught even a minnow with his bait.

They drove through crowded towns where the streets seethed with endless figures.

"Mam, all those people," he kept saying. He hadn't known there were so many people in the world.

They came at the end of the day to a tower that flared into the sky. It was so high that Barrie's head ached from trying to see the top. Up and up it went.

"Mam," he said. "Is that the Palace? Is that where the Queen lives?"

"Indeed no, boy bach," Mam said. "It's just an old block of flats."

Barrie didn't know what a flat was. He would remember for ever the panic terror of the lift as the doors swished shut and it shot into the sky, leaving most of him on the floor where he had started. He was surprised to find he was all in one piece.

In the eight years he had lived there he had never learned to like the lift. He was almost thirteen, but he had never forgotten the valley. One day, he would go back, and find it again. He would never find Meg and Bob. They must have died long ago. The house, Mam said, must have fallen into ruin, unless it had been bought by some rich city merchant for his holiday home.

The fortune Da had come to make never materialised. There were so few jobs a retired farmer could possibly do, especially one who had been forced off the land by failure. Da became a postman. He was in charge of all the men in the big sorting office now, and Mam worked in a shop. Living in a city took so much money. They were always tired at night and somehow, they no longer laughed as they had laughed in the valley. Mam looked out at the drab ground below the flats where the earth was bare and the grass worn away, and thought of the flowers by the Elwyn brook in the springtime, and she had no time for friends. She was always busy. Barrie longed for home made bread and the warm farmhouse smells but those too had gone. Da worked long hours and was often on duty at night. Barrie was lonely now.

Chapter 2

He went to the big school, but he hated that too. The boys in the London suburb laughed at his Welsh accent and at his towhead, for his hair was so fair that it was almost white. The brown country glow had long gone from his face and childish illnesses hit him worse than most as in the valley there had never been a single germ. He was so ill when he had measles he had to go to hospital. He hated that too. When he recovered he needed glasses as the germs had affected his eyes.

Towhead, glasses and a Welsh accent made him everybody's butt. His only friend was a boy called Walt, but Walt was far from clever and difficult to talk with. As he grew older, Barrie dreamed more and more about the valley. It had been so quiet there and the birds sang and

17

he loved the wild call of the curlew, the bird of the moors, Mam called it.

Here there was only the incredible din of the starlings flying back to roost in the town rooftops at night, their wings darkening the sky, their screams drowning the constant roar of traffic; the only other noise was the coo of the shabby town-dirty pigeons, ragbags of sooty feathers, that also spent their time commuting between the ledges and the streets. They were the only non-human creatures in the flats. No pets were allowed, not even white mice or a hamster. Barrie missed the farm beasts even more than he missed the valley.

When he was eleven years old he changed schools and from being one of the biggest boys at the primary school he became one of the smallest at the comprehensive. He still had two languages. Even Da was homesick for Wales and in the evenings they often spoke in their own lilting tongue and sang the songs that they had learned in the village choir. Singing was one of Barrie's few joys.

He sang in the school choir and sometimes sang solo and the clear bell-like notes floated above him, releasing all the tension and fear, so that for a little while, he felt as he used to feel when running on the high hills among the moss and heather with the farm dogs by his side.

Soon he had three languages. It was easier to try and mimic the other boys and speak as they did, in the oddly flat nasal whine that so grated on Mam's ears, and only revert to his own lilt when he was at home with Mam and Da and the rest of the world was safely shut away, beyond the bolted and chained front door. They had never locked a door on the farm. Here, no one dared leave the door open as thieves came in to steal.

It was the lilting Welshness that came out of him sometimes that formed an unexpected bond between Barrie and his new biology master. David Griffiths was an exile too. His name was Dafydd, but he had changed that. It did not do to own an unusual name among so many boys. David Griffiths was small and dark and bearded and had merry brown eyes behind very thick spectacles and an unexpectedly deep voice. He also sang in the choir, and his throbbing bass earned him the nickname Growler.

"You like animals, boy?" he asked, bumping into Barrie who was just slipping out of the biology lab, hoping to remain unseen. He came in every day at four o'clock so that he could open the cage and talk to the rabbits. He could never resist picking up Brownie, whose soft fur was so like Meg's. That night he had spent too long stroking her and had forgotten to look at the time and here was old Growler coming to lock up and here was Barrie where he had no right to be. He stopped, guilty feeling, and the red blush dyed his face and left it whiter than before.

"I'm not blaming you, boy. Only asking," Griffiths said, annoyed with himself. The boy was like a little dog, tail between legs, afraid of a cross word and no doubt teased constantly and maybe worse by some of the older lads, and louts they were, too, many of them, finding it funny to bully and bruise and hurt someone smaller than themselves who couldn't hurt back. Gave them a power feel, big brave creatures, clever enough to tread on an ant or kill a bee, but afraid themselves of anyone bigger or stronger.

"Come and help me clean the cages, boy, and feed the creatures, and fetch their water. Or is your mother expecting you? You don't want her to worry."

Barrie looked up. There was nothing but kindness in the brown eyes.

"Mam's at work," he said and the Growler sighed. Nothing was like it used to be. His own mother had always been at home, filling the house with warmth and fire-glow and the smell of cooking; of crispy rolls and of new-made cakes and meals fit for a king to offer his friends. Now David Griffiths lived by himself in a lonely room where the heat came out of a gasfire when you put a ten-pence piece in the meter and no one but himself cooked for him.

"Did you live in Wales?" David Griffiths asked, wanting to put this lost puppy child at ease, wanting to build confidence, wanting to soothe as he might have stroked a frightened dog and gentled it.

"I lived on a farm in Wales," Barrie said. "We had a pig and cows and two dogs and sheep. Only the winter killed the sheep and Da hadn't enough money and the bank wouldn't wait."

"Too bad, boy," Griffiths said and meant it most sincerely. "You'll miss the farm. But, do you know, I think you're just the boy for me. I need a reliable boy, a boy to feed the animals and clean the cages, and to bring them water. The other boys forget. But you'll know you can't forget animals. They sicken and die. And it's lonely for them here in the school. They need people who care. What do you say, boy?"

Say? Barrie couldn't say anything. He had been transported to next door to Heaven and next door to Heaven had five rabbits and six guinea pigs and six hamsters and twelve mice and eight jerbils. Creatures that ate and breathed and had babies, and that jumped about their cages and that liked being held and liked being fussed and liked being talked to. Creatures that would take some of the time out of the dreary day and absolve him from the horror of long lunch breaks in the playground not knowing who was going to jump on him or pull his hair or laugh at him, or punch him, or bloody his nose or steal his chocolate and twist his wrist and tell him he'd get done if he told. He never told, but it was hard sometimes to think up reasons for his bruises and Mam must have thought he spent his life walking into trees and lampposts. If she suspected anything else, she never said.

Barrie looked at the cages. A real farm was real Heaven, but next door held enormous promise. He stared up at Growler, wondering if he had heard properly. The Growler smiled at him.

"Well, boy? Is it a deal?"

"It's a deal," Barrie said. His heart was thumping so hard he was sure it must be moving his jersey. To be with beasts again, even if they were only small beasts, meant more than he could say.

"Can I start now?" he asked.

The Growler nodded.

"I'll do some marking," he said. "Then you can ask me for anything you can't find."

The late afternoon sun shone through the long uncurtained windows, shone on battered benches and stained sinks and bottles and jars. The school had spread into an old building and the animals had the worst of it, but Barrie did not care. He whistled as he cleaned the cages and spread the sawdust; he sang "All Through the Night" in Welsh as he washed the water bowls and filled them. He grinned till his mouth threatened to stretch across the whole of his face as he lifted each animal and held it against him, cuddling its small warm body, feeling the fur, and the slender bones beneath. He watched the jerbils jump; and the hamster in the far cage, indignant, drag all the cottonwool out of one jar and put it in the other. Barrie had filled the wrong one. The tiny creature worked busily. So did Barrie. It was years since he had known such pleasure. His farming ancestry was strong, making him yearn for work with living beasts, and now he knew that whatever happened and however Da planned, he had to get back, back to the land even if it were as a cowman on someone else's farm. Nothing else had any meaning.

One of the rabbits kicked and scratched as he picked it up. He gentled it, knowing its fear, talking softly, hissing as his grandfather had hissed when he groomed a horse. He remembered his Granda well, a tiny man with a wrinkled leathery face, and such a way with a horse that he was asked to master all the difficult steeds in Wales. There was always some rogue in his stables being taught manners. He had promised that Barrie should learn to ride, but he had died just before Da left Wales for ever and they discovered that Granda too had been beaten by time and there was little enough money to settle the debts for food for the beasts and for shoeing the horses. Nothing had gone right after Granda died.

David Griffiths persuaded Barrie to find a way of earning money and take the train into the country. The country was too far and too expensive, but Barrie washed cars and earned enough to go to Hampstead Heath where he looked for dandelion leaves for the rabbits. He found a fox's earth and was almost sure he had found a badger's sett, and the air was almost clean.

On his way home he bought the outside leaves of cabbages from the greengrocers. They came to know him and saved their throwaways so that his rabbits fed royally. Sometimes, if he had enough money over, he bought a tiny bunch of flowers for Mam.

Mam loved the flowers. She had plants in pots in the windows and everything she grew bloomed for her.

"Megan, girl, you're wasted here," Morgan Evans said to her, often. She looked at him and smiled. She had changed her job and now worked in a flower shop. It was better, but it wasn't the same, and when she looked out at the flats around her, at the ugly concrete blocks that towered into the sky, she saw instead a tiny farmhouse in a sheltered valley and the Elwyn brook bubbling over sun-brown stones, and the sheep on the hillside. She looked at her husband and smiled.

"No use crying over ill luck," she said. "You have to make the best of it."

For all that she and Barrie often went to the Park when they had time and sat by the lake, among the flowers, under the green trees, and watched the ducks on the water, and remembered the valley. Barrie, lying with daisies under his chin, and geese swimming near him and the sky high and blue above him.

Barrie wondered where he could find cattle; were there cattle in the lake near home, not here but his real home in the valley? When he was small he thought he might run away and dive deep and see if he could not find the lady and her cows and bring the cows for Da. Then he grew up and understood, and understanding hurt because he knew that Da also longed for his cows. He still brought home the farming journals and would sit for hours on a Sunday looking at the pictures of sleek prize winners and every year they went to the Dairy Show and spent an afternoon smelling the warm smell of cattle and seeing the sleek hides and brown long-lashed eyes and friendly faces of the gentle milkers. Every year Da came home silent and said never again and every year they argued, and finally took the train and went and lost themselves among their kind of people and Da talked farm talk and milking yields and spoke of cows he had had, once, long ago.

And every year Mam said she could not bear to go to the Park in daffodil time but every year they went and Mam looked and what she said was not "there's lovely it is," but "there's lovely it was," as she remembered the valley and wild daffodils shining on the side of the mountain and soft grey green pussy willow catkins feathery with pollen and primroses hiding under their leaves. Bluebells grew thick in the woods and in high summer there were harebells, and always the curlew crying to the wind that swept over the valley and ruffled the steel grey water of the lake.

Da saw the flowers and remembered walking in the lambing field and taking the new orphans home to the big kitchen and the laughter when they pulled and sucked at the bottles, in the warm old room that always smelled of bread.

Barrie did not remember the flowers or the sheep. He remembered the running water cold on his bare feet and the sheepdogs herding him and the old pig grunting, and the hunger grew in all of them, but it grew most of all, in Barrie, until it was an ache that could never be stilled.

"Can't we go back?" he asked.

Da said nothing, only pulled at his pipe and his face grew still and it was Mam who answered.

"Never go back, boy bach," she said. "It's never wise to go back."

Chapter 3

Wise or not to go back, Barrie didn't know. All he knew was that, as he grew older, the need for animals about him, for wide fields and high mountains and clean air and the Elwyn brook, grew stronger. Thousands of years of farming ancestors were crying in him to be free, crying to get away from the city streets and the tall tower blocks and the crowding people on every side, crying for the sheep among the rocks and the lark in the sky and the trees that were stunted and bare and close to the hill and torn by the wind from Tryfan. The cruel wind that warped the trees and combed the hedges flat against the little walls, but was far kinder than the wind that blustered in the city streets and tossed the rubbish flung by the casual crowds who did not care if their pavements were marred with paper and foul with debris, who did not glance aside, or smile, as the country people had smiled, who did not care at all about one another, but each about themselves and the money that gave them power over others. Money for motor bikes and for Bingo and for things that meant nothing to Barrie. He wanted money too, but money to spend on sheep and cows and a little farmhouse snug under the hill and looking towards the mountains. It was a need that grew; a need that was too big for him; a need that was a driving ache. He hated the city more every day.

It helped to be with David Griffiths who had also lived in Wales; who knew the story of the lady of the lake and the tales of the hills, and the princes who lived in the mountains, and knew too Barrie's favourite story of the hound Gelert who had saved his master's baby from a wolf, and lain by the cradle covered in blood, so that the Prince thought his child was dead and killed the dog and only then found the wolf lying dead and the child unharmed, and knew such remorse that he buried the dog with all honour. If Barrie ever had a dog again he would call him Gelert. When he grew up he would get away from the soulless flats and find a home where he could keep a dog. He needed a dog as much as he needed cattle and sheep, and Da worried because all Barrie's reading was about farms and farmland and he brought home books on pigs and on lambing and on breeding cattle, and learned about silage and balanced diets and many things that Da had never known in all his farming life, and only came to life when the talk turned to the land again. It was not good or wise, Mam said, frowning. They would never have money enough to farm again and land prices going up daily and nothing to rent, and nothing behind them, boy bach, will ye listen to me and not be so headstrong? It's for your own good. But Barrie heard nothing but the wind over the hills and the sound of sheep and he did not want to listen. It was no longer an ache but a raging need, and David Griffiths was the only one who knew and recognised it, and who watched daily as Barrie tended the animals and wondered if he had been wise to allow such a longing to arise. The boy was a farmer born and nothing would change it and life was too unfair.

Barrie washed more cars when he had time at weekends, wanting the money now for books. Books about livestock. Books about ploughing and reaping, about seeding and harvest and country stories about farmers.

"Do you think we did wrong?" he heard Da say one night, as he undressed for bed in the next room. The walls were thin and every word was audible, even next door where they were always shouting at each other and the children were always crying. Barrie that night had told them of Susie the white rabbit doe and her five new babies. They had moved her, he and David Griffiths, to a quiet corner of the staff cloakroom where she would be undisturbed. She had eaten her first litter and they did not want it to happen again. The Growler thought she had been unnerved because all the children wanted to see her, and had come in to look. "The boy needs beasts," Da said, through the wall, thinking Barrie was safely asleep.

Mam sighed, a sigh so big it floated on the air and hung there, sorrowful.

"We could have stayed," she said. "No use fretting. We did what we had to do and what we thought best. Don't you miss the beasts, too?"

"I miss it all, girl," Da said. "I think of the cows every night, of my Buttercup, and Cowslip with the crooked horn, and little Bluebell whose calves were nearly always white. I think of the dogs . . . I miss those dogs, girl, not the same, is it, without a dog to call to heel? And I think of the milk filling the buckets and the clank of the old machine. But it's no use thinking. We have a good life, and the money's good here. And not the worry we had, making ends meet and the lambs dying in the winter frosts and the wind from old Tryfan tearing the heart out of you when you were working in the snow about the farm. It's better here."

"Is it?" Mam said, and her voice was wistful, a little voice that looked back, remembering the warm kitchen and the cats underfoot and the singing in the chapel, and the neighbours who cared enough to come and call and bring a piece of the daughter's wedding cake, or asked you to the christening of the newest baby, or who came to help when a man was ill and the farm untended. No one bothered here.

It's not living, Barrie thought, lying looking into the dark. There was a wind here that screamed angrily round the corners and shook the block at night so that he was more afraid it might fall than he had ever been afraid of old Tryfan glowering above them, dominating the sky. There were other towers close, hiding the sun, casting long shadows of cold across his room, and he could see their lights going out one by one. Unfriendly lights belonging to strangers, not like the little lights on the mountain, the lights from Ty Gwyn and Eryri, from Plas Coch and Bryn Eglwys, the lights of Mair Pritchard and Dai Williams and old Mr. Jones the Post and Evans the Eggs and Ianto the Chickens. Barrie could remember them all. Mair Pritchard sang to him and told him stories of Old Wales, and Mr. Jones always wished him a happy birthday and added his own card to those that came by post, and Evans the eggs saved him two speckled brown eggs although they had chickens of their own and Ianto the chickens took him to see where the vixen had her cubs and they played on the hillside and Ianto the chickens made Barrie sit tighter than a henbird on her eggs and watch, and the cubs never caught the scent of them on the wind, and that day too Barrie learned to hide his scent from an animal and how to test the wind

26

and know which way it was blowing.

Now old Mair Pritchard was dead and Evans must be a very old man, sitting by his fireside, remembering the days when he was young and could stride the mountains and had mastered Tryfan, climbing to the top and down again, and Ianto the chickens had had to give up his farm too and had gone to Canada to make his fortune, but no fortune came to him either and he was driving a bus in Toronto, and wrote on Barrie's birthday, as he was Barrie's god-father and Mam's first cousin. They were all close in the valley.

Barrie could not sleep. He got out of bed and looked down from the window at the far below seething road where cars zipped past every minute and horns sounded and brakes protested and tyres screamed. There were no owls in this sky. There were no flowers on the muddy ground where the boys played and rubbed away the grass that had once been laid to soften the concrete desert that stretched for miles.

Barrie thought of the park and the coolness under the trees and the small delightful chocolate coloured poodle who had romped with him the previous weekend while his owner sat and watched, smiling, glad that her dog had a boy to play with. Jasper, the poodle was called. A charmer. A dog. That was what he needed. He must have a dog. It would make the city at least endurable until he grew up and could get away.

"There's daft, boy," Mam said, becoming very Welsh when something annoyed her, as it often did these days. She brushed her hair back out of her eyes. Her hair was growing very grey. Even Barrie noticed that. "How can you have a dog in a flat? Be reasonable, boy. They won't even let you keep a hamster here."

"Can't we move, Mam? To a house, and a garden? We don't have to stay here. Why do we stay here?" Barrie knew his parents both hated living in a flat.

"Because houses cost money, boy. We won't ever have money for a house so stop your fretting. And you can never have a dog. Dogs need country to run in and plenty of room

27

and cost money to feed. It's not right to keep them in streets and houses. It would be cruel." Mam went out of the room and slammed the kitchen door hard behind her, not wanting Barrie to see her sudden tears. It was hard on the boy and it was hard on his Da and it was hard on her. She was not angry with Barrie but with the cruel modern world that made life so difficult. But Barrie went to his room, thinking she was angry with him and sat on his bed and took up the book he had taken from the school library. It was called HOW TO TRAIN YOUR DOG. Brett Taylor, a big bully from another class, had seen the book and sniggered.

"Got a dog then, Taffy?" he asked. He tweaked Barrie's ear hard, just to make sure he heard and understood. Barrie wriggled free and the red blush dyed his face as it always did when he was hurt or angry.

"I'm going to get one," he had said.

"A diddy little pooch for a diddy little Mammy's boy," Brett said. His thick arm reached out and his mutton fist pulled Barrie's glasses off, and waved them a few feet from his face. "You need a seeing eye dog, don't you, Taffy? Blind as a bat, aren't you, Taffy? Can you see your glasses, Taffy? Come and get them, then, ask for them on your knees, Taffy, or I'll twist your wrist and make you yell for help. You'll need your seeing eye dog, won't you, Taffy, when I've smashed your glasses."

Luckily for Barrie a door opened and the Growler came out. He had a fine angry stare on him and he stared hard now at Brett, and held out his hand for Barrie's glasses.

"I'll take those," he said, in a deep ominous voice. "Get out, before something nasty happens to you."

Brett gave the Growler a glare and handed him the glasses and hurried off. Barrie discovered that his heart was thumping and that he felt sick. He put his glasses on miserably. One of the lenses had cracked and Mam would complain about the money it cost to repair them. Something was always happening to his glasses. The other boys thought it funny to grab and leave him floundering without them They never realised how Barrie hated having to wear them

28

and hated being unable to see. He looked miserably up at the Growler, wanting to thank him, but not knowing how without sounding silly, so he said nothing.

"Come and feed Susie," David Griffiths said. "Her babies are getting quite big. We'll have to do something about them soon." He ignored Barrie's tight mouth and the hand that rubbed across his eyes leaving a dirty streak across his face.

It was quiet in the staff cloakroom where Susie was blissfully feeding her babies. They were now large bundles of white fluff, and recognised Barrie and came to greet him and to nuzzle his finger. Susie always came towards him, knowing he brought her greens. He filled her water bowl and put her in the second cage and cleaned and scrubbed the first and left it by the radiator to dry. He took three times as long as usual and by the time he had finished everyone also had gone home, and he could walk in peace with no one to bother him. He went out into the playground. There were four boys waiting by the gate. Brett Taylor was one of them. Barrie went back into the cloakroom. David Griffiths was putting on his coat.

"I'll give you a lift," he said, and Barrie went out with him into the car park and drove safely past the four of them, who watched him, grins on their faces that assured him they would remember, and that tomorrow they would be waiting and the day after that, and the day after that. And for always.

Barrie shivered as he lay in bed reading his book. He hated fighting. And they were all much bigger than he. He shut his mind to them and thought about his dog. House training was easy. His dog would be so intelligent he would soon learn that. And he would learn to sit and to come to heel. If he had a dog, a really big dog, an Alsatian or a Dobermann Pinscher, a fierce dog his dog who would protect him against bullies like Brett. It would growl at the flick of a finger, snarl at the twitch of an eyebrow, be guardian and watchdog and companion, all in one. It would be a terror, a real terror. It would be strong enough to kill a wolf, like Gelert, and faithful until death, like

Gelert. It would be a one man dog, acknowledging no one else, obeying only him, waiting for him outside the school gate, flying to him when he whistled. He would name it Gelert.

That night, Gelert was born. Born ready grown and ready trained and ready for anything.

Chapter 4

Gelert was fully grown, and very real, although he only existed in Barrie's mind. He was a handsome Alsatian, lean, strong and sleek. He had wise warm brown eyes and no one existed for him in the world but Barrie. He walked to heel, close against Barrie's leg, leaning sometimes, looking up, watching all the while, never taking his eyes off his master, ready to obey. He was so real that Barrie could see him, could feel his presence at his heels, would turn his head to watch the dog come into the room, and lie quiet, out of sight behind his father's chair.

Barrie began to live in his dreams. Reality was no kind of fun. Reality was other boys bullying, was the class laughing horridly at his mistakes, at his accent when he slipped into his Welsh lilt, reality was being Taffy and Towhead and Goggles and Foureyes, not to mention worse words that, if he ever used at home, forgetting, made Mam wash his mouth with soap or Da flip him, angry, across the wrist with a leather glove that hurt.

"It's coarse and nasty they are down here," Mam said. "Not like our lads in the valley. I'll not be having you grow up like them. Do that and you'll never go back, if that's what you're after and you're as obstinate as your Da. But they'll not have you. No time for city manners in the valley, boy, and don't you forget it. If you can call them manners. I don't know what's got into people. There's no kindness left."

Mam dreamed too, Barrie could tell, when she looked out of the window, her eyes wistful, looking down at the bare mud where once grass had been planted, at the ruined trees that the lads had torn to pieces, at the high enclosing walls of the towering flats opposite, each flat in it a replica of their flat. Everything the same, everywhere, everyone living the same way, going to work and coming home and maybe stopping for a drink at the local, or spending an evening watching the telly. Call that living, Barrie thought, and whistled his dog to him, and Gelert was so real that Mam and Da became a little unreal and he did not always hear them, because he was walking under Tryfan's towering cliffs with Gelert beside him and they had flushed a hare from the bushes and he could see it running, loping through the heather, turning briefly to see if he were following, as he pounded up the slope, his heart thumping. Then the hare would leap a wall and leap the Elwyn brook and he would take pity on it and call Gelert back to him and they would run and roll together, the dog warm and hard against him, putting his paws on Barrie's shoulders, looking up into his face, or walking alongside, playing with Barrie's fingers and his own lead. Every evening Barrie trained his dog rigorously. Taught him to sit and to heel, and the dog was more real than ever, so real that Barrie went and stood outside the Parish Hall where they held an obedience class and watched people drive up with their dogs, and go inside, and thought that Gelert was more handsome than any of these.

It was difficult to turn away, and realise that Gelert did not exist.

One night, when thin rain was drenching out of a sulky sky, Barrie moved into the shelter of the porch.

He had forgotten about Brett. He had forgotten about school. He had been thinking about his Alsatian, thinking so hard that he could almost feel the dog beside him, close against him looking into his face. He put down a hand and desolation swept him as he felt nothing. He watched the lucky owners coming in with their dogs. They smiled at him. He was, by now, well known to them. He had waited outside so often, not speaking, just looking. Everyone thought he belonged to someone else, or was waiting for a friend, and he had never been inside the hall, although he longed to go, and sit in that charmed company and watch the other owners train their dogs so that when he was grown, and had his own, he would know how to set about it.

Books were all very well, but books didn't allow for the dog himself or the difference between dogs, and Da often talked of training sheepdogs and how one was easy and one was hard and one had an eye for the sheep and another played the fool and the first he ever trained had to be sold as he was a prize Trial dog, able to work with a small flock on a competition field, but useless on the hills where he needed to range far and bring in the sheep that had strayed from their bases, and gone higher up the mountain. Some dogs were bold and others timid; some biddable and some arrogant. Just like people. Sometimes he preferred dogs to people, but a dog was only a dog, and at least he could talk to Walt. But Walt wasn't allowed to go out at night.

The sudden brutal clasp on his arm made Barrie jump. He turned his head and there was Brett and three of the other boys in his form, which was one above Barrie's. Brett was grinning, and there was nobody about. The obedience class had started. Barrie could hear the thump of feet and the commands from inside, commands like drill at school.

Left about turn. Watch your dogs. Handlers and dogs, forward. Tell your dogs to stay. Last commands to your dogs.

"I've got to go in," Barrie said breathlessly. "Someone's holding Gelert for me. I came out to look for Walt. He's coming to watch tonight."

The words fell over one another. Barrie was so afraid he felt sick. There were four of them and only one of him and no one was about. The rain-lashed streets were cold and wet and empty and the streetlights shone with a blue glow that chilled the night, and Brett was so close to him that his face loomed enormous, wide red mouth a-grin with glee, shock-mane black hair damp against his head. The other boys were watching, grinning hard, as Brett twisted again.

"You haven't got a dog at all, Cowardy Taffy. Taffy was a Welshman, Taffy was a liar. Invented your dog to scare us, didn't you, Taffy Liar? Think we don't know you can't have a dog in the flats, Taffy Liar? Think we haven't watched you, standing outside here every Wednesday, watching the people and never going in? Thought you'd fool us, didn't you, Taffy thief, Taffy liar, Taffy coward? Well you haven't. We've found you out."

They moved closer, menacing, and Brett pulled Barrie's glasses off and waved them in front of his face. They were so engrossed they did not see the small red van draw up, did not see the man who looked over at them and leaped out fast, whistling two enormous Alsatians out of the back of the van and to his heel. The sudden angry barking shocked all four of them.

"All right, lads," the man said. He loomed over them, and they suddenly shrank back to boysize in Barrie's eyes. He saw fear grow as the two growling Alsatians closed in. Brett let go of Barrie's wrist and jumped away and Barrie stood dumb, massaging the red mark that was growing into a bruise and that ached.

"What's it about then?" the man asked, his voice angry.

"He says he's got an Alsatian, a big brute called Gelert that will go for us if we touch him," Brett said sulkily. "He's a liar. He lives in the flats and he hasn't got a dog at all."

"That's what you think," the man said sharply. He had seen the fear in Barrie's eyes, the red mark on his wrist, and he had seen Brett snatch the boy's glasses from his face. He took the glasses and handed them back to Barrie.

"This is Gelert," he said, pointing to the biggest of the two dogs. "I kennel him, that is all. Now get off, the lot of you. We have work to do."

"He said his dog was inside," Brett said mutinously, his eyes on Barrie's face.

"He wasn't sure what time I'd come," the man said. "What else would he do with a gang of little thugs like you? Think it's clever don't you, to bully someone smaller than yourself. Four to one, and him younger than you. Stone me, I've a good mind to set the dogs on you and don't think I wouldn't. Now, do you go, or do I tell my dog to jump you? I daren't tell Gelert. He saw what you did to his owner, and he'd eat the lot of you. Listen to him."

The big Alsatian was growling fiercely. Barrie saw the man cock a finger, and the dog inched forward and barked noisily, angrily and the four turned and ran, the sound of their thudding feet dying away in the distance. Barrie was suddenly shaking and his knees belonged to somebody else. He leaned against the wall, and within an instant both dogs were quiet, and the big one, that the man had said was called Gelert, was nosing him, his brown eyes friendly. Barrie stroked his head, pretending for one brief moment that this was really his dog, was his Gelert come to life, and then the tears came, and he had to turn away and choke into the darkness, and the man lit a pipe and stood smoking, saying nothing, until Barrie could stand up again, and grin sheepishly, and say thank you, mister, meaning it with all his heart.

The man looked down at him.

"You like dogs," he said, stating a fact, not asking a question.

Barrie nodded.

"Is his name Gelert?" he asked, settling his glasses back on his nose and sniffing desperately. The man handed him a handkerchief.

"No, it's Rocha," he said, pronouncing the word rocker. "But it was worth a try. They bother you much?"

Barrie nodded again.

"I thought . . . if they thought I had a dog . . .?" he said, and the man nodded again, remembering his own boyhood and the hoodlums he had to use the dogs on at night. He was a dog guard, working for the local council, patrolling the parks against vandals and Barrie could now see the words on the van. Mobile Dog Patrol.

"I teach here," the man said. "A good job I was late tonight. I had to go out to a school that had a break-in. Where do you live?"

Barrie pointed to the towers that dominated the skyline, about half a mile away. The man looked across and nodded.

34

He was an understanding sort of man. Both Alsatians were now at his side, watching for him, waiting for his commands, slightly puzzled because they had not gone inside the Hall at once, as soon as the boys had gone. The man looked up at the flats. He hated high tower buildings, and thought the planners were raving mad, believing this was excellence and a lovely place for people to live, not knowing they were making soul-destroying prisons, centrally heated little cages where men and women and children could pass the time until they died, never having known that there was a world beyond the endless streets, never owning a dog or a cat, never having the responsibility of rearing a small defenceless creature that relied on them for its very existence.

Barrie found himself suddenly telling the Alsatian owner about the valley and about Meg and Bob who must now be dead, but who had been such wonderful dogs, herding the sheep, dropping at a whistle, coming to a call, both with the sheepdog eye that could quell a ram and make him settle down and come where they wanted and not go his own way. He thought miserably about the flats and how there was no longer any colour in Mam's cheeks and no light or laughter, ever, in Da's eyes, and no dog to play with, and desolation made his throat ache.

"We can't go back, ever," he said. "But Mam and Da, they don't like it here either. There are no beasts, you see."

The man nodded. He did see. He owned eight Alsatians which he kept in a big kennel behind his house, an old house in Blackheath. He liked the towheaded boy with his serious face, and he liked the way the boy spoke to the dogs.

"Lots of people distrust Alsatians," he said. "Would you like to help me? Would you like to show the people inside how good a really well trained dog can be? These will work for anyone. Which will you handle first?"

Barrie stared at him. David Griffiths had opened one gate to Heaven and here was another, being offered free. He couldn't believe his luck. For a few minutes, his dream would come true. He would have to return to bleak reality afterwards, but at least, for a brief moment, he would have a dog. He put his hand on the head of the one that looked like Gelert, as he had imagined Gelert to be and the man laughed.

"You've an eye for a good dog, son," he said. "That's my best Alsatian. Rocha's a champion. Come on in. What's your name?"

Barrie told him.

"And I'm Mike Allerton," the man said.

They went inside.

Inside was a big bare hall and a bare wood floor and chairs against the walls and people sitting on them, each with a dog. There were as many women as men, and as many dogs as people. Sealyhams and terriers, Labradors and retrievers, Alsatians and Jack Russells and ordinary mongrelly whippety dogs with kind faces and merry eyes and happily wagging tails. Barrie had never seen so many dogs together in his life, all quiet, all behaving perfectly, their owners watching as he walked in with Mike. He was conscious of his worn jeans and old jersey and his towhead and his glasses.

He stood quietly, holding Rocha, while Mike spoke to the people he knew, and then walked the second dog beside him, close at heel.

"Now I'll show you what a natural trainer can do with a dog," Mike said, suddenly. "Barrie's a farmer's son. He was brought up with sheepdogs and he has the handler's eye. This fellow of mine isn't easy to take on. I spent days training him, but Barrie can handle him. He can handle any of my dogs. Watch Barrie work Rocha."

Barrie was beginning to enjoy himself for the first time for years. He walked into the centre of the floor as Mike spoke, and followed Mike's directions, circling the room, turning left, right and left again and all the time the Alsatian followed him, as if he were glued to the boy's leg, not an inch of light showing, sitting when told, turning when Barrie turned.

More than ever Barrie longed for a dog. This was achievement, and it would be an even greater achievement to take a new and untrained pup and teach it and bring it to perfection. He looked up at Mike as he passed and Mike looked back and knew that this boy needed animals far more than most boys, that he was part of the animal world and would have to belong, no matter where, or how. He had to be found a niche of his own.

Mike knew how Barrie felt. He had grown up with only one dog in the house, always a small dog. He had met a local Alsatian breeder when he was nine years old and from then on had haunted the kennels, had played with the puppies and romped with the older dogs. By the time he was twelve he chose to help at the kennels rather than join his friends in their paper rounds. He learned all the time; learned about feeding dogs and breeding dogs and by the time he was sixteen he was helping handle the dogs at Shows and five years later was given a pup of his own as a reward for his long service, as a twenty-first birthday present.

Mike had had to work with dogs. He tried several jobs but none of them were rewarding. He worked in a bank; he gave that up and drove a hire car; he gave that up too, and worked full time at the kennels; handled dogs for other breeders, travelling the country from Show to Show, grooming the champions until one day he sold a young Alsatian to the local police force and the sergeant offered to help him train his dogs for relief guard work. From then, Mike had never looked back.

He came with his dogs to guard wedding presents; to keep gate crashers out of Hunt Balls; to patrol the local parks and enclosed spaces; to patrol schools and factories and other vulnerable buildings, and now, watching Barrie, he knew just how he felt and remembered the all-consuming hunger he had had to work with dogs. He would give the boy a chance, just as Captain Martin, all those years ago, had given Mike a chance.

"How about fish and chips?" Mike asked, as they stood outside in the rainy dark with the street lamps casting dazzles over the wet pavement. "Will your parents be wondering where you are?"

"They think I'm at the pictures," Barrie said. He had intended to go and see the Western that was on at the Regina, but he had been diverted by the dogs. It was going to be very hard to go home to the empty flat.

"Would you like to come and help with my dogs?"
Mike asked, suddenly well aware that Wednesday evenings
would never be enough, would only whet Barrie's longing,
would make the long empty week much worse. "It's not
far by train, on a Saturday, if your folk don't mind."

Barrie would come if Tryfan fell tomorrow and reached
far enough to blot out all the flats. He would come through
flood and hell-fire and high water, he would come through
snow and sleet and rain, he would come no matter what
Mam said, or Da said, if it only meant being with dogs,
helping with dogs, walking with dogs, one step towards
the farm he would have when he grew up and the sheep he
would raise. He was saving every penny he could, after he
had paid his fares and for birthday and Christmas presents,
and one day he would have enough to buy a farm and take
Mam and Da back to where they belonged and everything
would be the same again, just as it had been when he was
small. Mam would bake and Da would help with the sheep
and the cows and they would train the dogs and it would be
the best farm in the whole of Wales. He knew much more
about farming now, and he could also figure and read and
write and work out the best way to make money and he
would be a success. He had to be a success. Meanwhile he
could start by learning all he could about dogs. Maybe if
he never became a farmer he could breed Alsatians, so that
should make money too.

"Thank you," Barrie said, his Welsh accent suddenly
strong because he was so excited. "I will come, indeed I
will. Every week. I promise."

Chapter 5

School was a long desert between the oasis on Wednesday
night and that at the weekends, when Barrie went out to
the kennels and scrubbed and cleaned and exercised the
dogs, and looked at the diet sheets, and walked on the Heath,

and listened to Mike. Mike talked about dogs he had known and dogs he had shown and dogs he had bred and dogs he worked with. He talked about his own dogs; about Rocha who had been abandoned in a local park and found by a farmer and adopted by Mike. About Pan, who had been thrown out of a car on the motorway and broken his leg, and Mike had nursed him back to health.

About Shan, whom Mike had bred himself; and the magnificent Tornado who had won Show after Show and died at twelve, a champion and father of champions. His photograph hung in the hall of Mike's big old house, where he lived with his sister, who taught at the local school and owned her own Alsatian, a gentle little bitch named Suki.

Between whiles, Barrie still dreamed about Gelert, and his own dog walked beside him when he went home, and walked beside him at school, and he only had to put a hand down, he knew, and he would feel the hard head and the soft fur, had only to turn his head and see the brown eyes. He was no longer afraid of Brett. He was supremely indifferent and because there was no fun in bullying someone who didn't care, he was left in peace. His only trouble now came from his bad schoolwork. He so often forgot to listen because he was thinking about the dogs.

"The boy might as well belong somewhere else," he heard Da say, exasperated, one night, through the thin dividing wall.

"He's happier," Mam said.

"And his school report is terrible," Da said angrily. Barrie heard him drop one shoe and then the other, heard the bedsprings creak as he climbed in. "He'll never go to College with school reports like that. All our trouble wasted."

"He wants to go to farming college," Mam said.

"There's no future in farming, girl," Da said in his most exasperated voice, and Barrie thought perhaps Da was trying to convince himself as much as Mam.

"Does that matter?" Mam asked. "It isn't a life we're living here, Morgan, and well you know it. You with your old letters every day, down in the sorting office, shut indoors and no fresh air to breathe and me in the shop. I like the flowers mind, I don't say I don't, but it's not the same. I think of the valley every day. And I hate the city and so does Barrie."

"It's a better life," Da said. "Better than starving in the country; better than working with lambs in the wicked wind from Tryfan, better than sitting watching the old mountain glower down at you every day and the rain lash out of the heavens and soak you and better than watching the lambs sicken and die and fighting the foxes, and knowing you only rear the beasts so that people can eat them. You never liked the sheep going to market, girl."

There was no more sound from his parents. Barrie lay and watched the lights flick out in the block that shadowed his window, and thought of Gelert, and how he would walk with him in the summer, in the Park. It was sometimes hard to believe that there would be no dog at his bedside if he put down his hand, no dog to come when he whistled. At weekends, walking Rocha, he pretended that Rocha was his, was his Gelert, come to life, and was happier than he had been for years. And the Heath was almost country with bushes and trees and wild flowers and the pool was a miniature Lyn Elwyn, and there were doves and magpies and blackbirds and once even a hare. Mike said she reared her babies every year and took them to feed in the gardens, but no one had the heart to kill her, nuisance though she was. She reminded too many people of the country.

"Time you spent a weekend with your Mam and with me," Da said one day. "Always running off to those old dogs."

"Not in the town, Da," Barrie said, pleading, longing to get away from the streets and shops and houses and too many people, always so noisy, and talk talk talking with nothing to say.

They took a train into the country, the real country, two hours from London, out from the rows of houses and into the fields, with the big trees that even now seemed strange remembering the stunted twisted trunks in the valley.

"Not like Wales," Mam said, wistful, looking out over the parkland. "No mountains." They were walking down a twisting lane and the hedges were green and the air was winesharp and exciting and a bird was singing.

"It's good land," Da said, bending and lifting a handful of soil and letting it trickle through his fingers. "Rich land. Growing land. Never see grass like this under Tryfan. Feeding land. Just look at those cows. There's a herd for a man to feast his eyes on. Never see cattle like that in the valley, girl."

Da walked to the fence, and leaned on the barred white gate and looked at the cows. Barrie, not looking behind, because he was pretending Gelert was running free, running over the grassland, racing against the wind, looked instead at his Da and saw the longing on his face come there and stay. Da looked at the cows as if he would take all of them and farm with them again. Barrie counted them. Thirty-two sleek Jersey cows with soft caramel coats and dark brown eyes. They came to the gate and huffed at them and Da drowned in the smell of them, the warm milky breath of them, the dark brown eyes of them, and Mam stroked the soft hides.

"There's lucky, the farmer is," Da said, and all the envy in the world was in his voice. "Such lovely beasts. There's luck."

Barrie put his hand down to feel Gelert's cold nose. The dog had been bounding after a rabbit, which Barrie had seen run from under the hedge. He was panting and breathless, and Barrie whistled between his teeth, wanting to call him off before he caught it. The bounding body had come back to his side, so real that he almost spoke, but he knew his parents would not understand. For all that the body that leaned against his leg was so real that he almost felt it. He put his hand down and touched the hard bony skull, covered by soft warm skin. Belief had materialised his dog. He looked down and jumped as a warm tongue licked his hand. A dog had come, out of thin air. This was no Alsatian, though, and not his Gelert. He had thought, for one heart-stopping instant in time, that he had wanted something so badly that he had made it happen. This dog was a coal black Labrador, all shining body and glowing eyes and gaily wagging tail.

"You like cows?" a voice said beyond Da, and Da jumped.

Barrie turned and found that the dog had left his side and was greeting a burly dark man, whose eyes were as brown and kind as those of his cattle, whose full lipped mouth was curved in a smile as he watched Da's face, whose hands were strong and darkened by sunshine that bathed them daily, and whose voice was low and throbbing and reminded him of the Growler. A man you could trust and a man the animals trusted as the sleek brown heads were thrusting against his arm, pushing against his hand, leaning over the fence, each cow jostling for the stroking he gave her.

"There's beauty," Da said, as a slender calf lifted its small head and gazed with shining eyes at the humans standing at the gate. And Barrie knew then that Da was as unhappy as he, that the longing in him had never been stilled, that going to the town had never been right, that Da wanted to go back too, back to the wide moors under the empty sky, back to the high hills and the wind that roared off Tryfan, back to the Elwyn brook and the little old farmhouse that had been home. Now, they had no home at all. They only had a place in which to sleep. And remember.

Barrie could not bear the look on his Da's face. The dog had come back to him, wagging its tail, thrusting an eager head at the boy, pushing, asking him to play, and Barrie dropped to his knees and put his arm round the Labrador's neck and gave himself a few minutes of total bliss. There would be pain when they had to go, but now there was only ecstasy, sharpened by the knowledge that the minutes were stolen from reality and this could not last.

The big man was smiling at Da and his brown eyes were friendly.

"I had my own farm, once," Da said, as if it were centuries ago, almost beyond memory. "In Wales, it was. But it was hard farming, and poor soil and the winters killed the young lambs, froze them on the hills, two years running, and we could not manage. Had to sell up. Silliest thing I ever did," Da said, bitter, and the first time ever admitting it, but admitting it now, and Barrie knew that he could no longer tease and worry, Da wanted to go back so much that he would if he could and he knew too that it was impossible. Have to stay in the horrid old town and make the best of it, and there was no hope, anywhere, ever. Not even the dog at his feet, looking up at him with lolling tongue and mouth a-gape and merry eyes, could keep the desolation from near overwhelming him with an ache so bad that he did not know how to bear it.

Da was still talking, talking out the hurt of years, talking to a man who would understand.

"It's no life for a man, away from beasts. Mine were nothing like these though, just rough old Welsh cattle. There's beauties these are. Make a man half die with longing, just to look at them. A man might give his chance of Heaven to work with beasts like these."

The hurt inside Barrie was worse. Da's eyes fair ate the cattle, and Mam's were tear filled and Barrie knew she could not see. He wanted to go to them both and hug them both and tell them he knew how they felt and he was sorry he had pestered so, he hadn't understood before, but it wasn't possible. There's daft they'd think him, making a fuss like a baby thing, and not a grown boy at all. He swallowed the ache.

Da was deep in cattle talk, talk of feed and milking yield and calving and Mam was running her hands over the golden heads, admiring the dark rings round the jewelled eyes, the beasts responding to her, rubbing against her, as they always had in the valley. All the cows knew her and let down their milk better for her than for anyone else, even than Da, and when a new beast was awkward and would not let the milk come then Mam's soft hands and Mam's soft voice gentled her and soothed her and won her trust, and the rich creamy stuff came from her swiftly into the bucket and Da would grin and say, "There's clever. I have the cleverest wife in the whole of the valley," and Mam would turn and look at him and smile and Barrie would feel a small twist of jealousy because they had only thoughts for each other and none for him and he was left out.

And then Mam would see him standing there, small and forlorn and reach out her arms and shelter him inside them and he was safe again and part of the family again and remembered again and Da would ruffle his hair and laugh and say, "We'll make a farmer of you yet, boy bach," and Barrie knew that all was well at home.

Nothing was like that now, and it was not only because he was thirteen and no longer a baby. There was no closeness between Mam and Da, no smiles exchanged as there used to be, only the three of them, each one lonely and longing to go back and each never saying.

The dog began to romp, running backwards front legs bent, barking and teasing Barrie, teasing him to run, to forget his woes. It was a lovely day and all the time in the world, and in a moment Barrie forgot he was grown and was back again with Meg and Bob, and was running as he had not run for years over the soft turf. He kicked off his hot socks and heavy shoes and felt the grass cool under his bare feet and he chased and rolled with the big dog, his mind only on the moment. He gave his glasses to Mam and was away, racing through the shallows of a tiny stream, the dog at his heels, barking with excitement, splashing through the ripples, shaking violently to dry his wet coat so that the bright drops flashed in the sun and soaked Barrie, who laughed and ran again, startling a kingfisher that perched, a blazing gem in the whispering willows.

When he was so hot he could only pant with the dog, he flung himself down and watched the arrowdart of fish in the ruffled water and felt the hot body of the dog close against him and heard the windsong in the telegraph wires and the birdsong in the bushes, and the clear song of the country was all around him, soothing away the tension of

44

years. Above him the blue sky was a-run with little clouds, clouds building together on the far horizon, threatening rain later in the day, but now the sun shone and there was peace, and a dog beside him, and the world was his to keep for a moment, to keep as he wanted it, and not as it was in the town.

The farmer took them back to the house for tea. Barrie had never seen such a house. It was vast and old, built before Cromwell stole England from the king, built of huge blocks of dressed stone with dark oak panelled rooms and furniture that once had gleamed and shone but now was sadly dusty.

In the big old fashioned kitchen there were stone flags on the floor and black sheepskin rugs to cover them near the fire and a tabby cat that stretched and rolled on to her back and purred contentedly as the farmer laughed and stroked her with a gentle foot, and the dog walked over and nosed her to greet her.

Barrie dropped to the hearth rug and sat crosslegged and the cat curled against him and the dog lay panting beside him and the talk flowed over him, flowed smoothly and gently, rising and falling, with silences and long comfortable pauses as once the talk had flowed in the kitchen of the little farmhouse that nestled against Tryfan's stern flanks.

Such talk as he had almost forgotten; of cattle and prices and hay and corn and new methods and old methods and milking machines and a new sort of milking parlour that neither Da nor the farmer seemed to like, and of weather and barley and maize and oats, of frost and snow and storm and harvest, until evening was on them and the cattle ripe for milking, coming to the farmer's call, full udders brimming and swinging, and Da went out to help and the yard was filled with the milking song that he always sang to his own cattle, a Welsh song that was near as old as Tryfan himself, and was so familiar that Barrie almost expected to see the horizon darken and the mountains loom black and feel the cold keen wind of the hills across his face.

The soft words filled the dusk and Mam and Barrie

listened and the cows listened too and let down their milk in a flowing continuous stream that filled the containers. Da had once been known as Evans the Song, when they lived in the valley, for his voice often sounded on the air and echoed back from the mountains, and it filled the little chapel until the roof rang with the glory of the sound and the majesty of the singing and Barrie knew that when the angels sang in Heaven they could sing no sweeter than his Da. He had been very small then, but Da's voice had lost nothing over the years and the tune and the words hung in the air, and the time stood still.

"There's been a long time since your Da sang," Mam said, and Barrie knew from her voice that she was full of tears. His own throat hurt. He went out to look at the cattle and the dog followed him, nosing his leg, delighted to have a boy about the place again.

The warm smell of the cows was memory made real again; the plunge and shuffle of the wide bodies, the swish of a tail, the twist of a head, the gaze of the mild eyes, and they might never have been away. It was all familiar, a part of them that came back without a single hesitation, a knowledge that was deeper than the lake that brooded under the far away mountains, a wisdom that need never be taught.

The machines pumped, their motors thumping, and the churns filled and the heady air was thick with the warmth of the cattle and the never forgotten scent of creamy yellow frothing milk that gushed so freely and was like nothing that ever came out of a bottle. The farmer gave Barrie a glass to fill for himself and back in a tumble came all the memories, standing small and shy watching the huge men talk, himself almost too small to see over the top of the white scrubbed kitchen table, in the kitchen in the farm in the valley.

He walked out into the yard. There was a boar in a sty, a young Large White, his face merry as he shoved his snout at a lever that filled his water bowl. He held his head beneath the clear stream and looked up from the miniature waterfall, and then bent his head and drank. Barrie stroked

46

the hard back, and picked up a stick and leaned over to scratch and the pig leaned against the stick and grunted with joy, rubbing himself against the sharp end that eased the perpetual itch along his spine.

"Your singing's produced more milk for me than I've ever seen," the farmer was saying in disbelief when they tidied the milking parlour. Mam had been unable to stay inside. She was taking the cattle back to the field calling gently, "Coom on then, coom on then," in a long soft croon, her face alive again, her eyes alight, colour flushing her cheeks. One of the cows pushed against her and her small hand touched the beast gently, lingering on the warm hide, as if longing to stay. She shook herself and walked on and the cows went with her, back to the calf-high grass, to drowse in the evening sun. The shadows were long, and there were other shadows in the sky as the clouds gathered, brooding, flinging high the anvil shapes that were the forerunners of storm.

"Thunderheads," Da said, looking upwards. The farmer nodded. The weather mattered all the time.

Barrie leaned against the five-barred gate and looked at the stone house, sprawling under a mass of trees. The once cared for garden was overgrown with weeds. There was grass in the cobbles, and only the dairy and milking parlour were clean. Mam had, without thinking, some time before, rubbed her finger along the oak chest in the hall and looked at the mark she had made in the dust.

"There's short of men and women to work here," she said, now, almost under her breath and when she had shut the gate she stood thoughtful, looking at her dusty finger and watching the cattle move away, and drop their heads to feed.

The farmer came and stood beside her. Soon they must go for their train, but there were a few moments left, moments to savour, moments that would have to last for many years. Barrie had put his glasses on again and now he felt stupid and shy. He was Towhead again and Goggles and Foureyes and daft old Taffy. He swallowed, and spoke.

"What's your dog's name?" he asked and the farmer

47

turned to look at the boy, realising how silent he had been, sitting there quietly, his face absorbed, listening, but saying nothing. Even now, he had spoken almost in a whisper.

"Terror," the farmer said and laughed. "He was a proper terror when he was a pup. Ate everything, including my best hat and the notebook of the man from the Ministry who called on me one day. I've taught him better now but he needs more training. I don't have time. I never have time. My last cowman left me three months ago and went to work in a factory, with shorter hours and evenings off and better pay. I can't get another, and I'm getting desperate."

He looked at Barrie's Da and Da looked at Mam and they both looked as if God had come down out of the sky and opened the gates of Heaven.

Barrie stood on one leg and held on to the dog, and said a quick prayer, a chapel prayer first in English and then in Welsh, just to make sure God would understand.

But he must have left something out.

Da looked at the grass growing in the cobbles and knew that the milking machine was old and needed replacing. He knew the byres needed repairing and that maybe there was no cowman here because there were no wages here either.

"I need a man, and help in the house," the farmer said. "My wife died two years ago, and I don't want another wife. No one can replace my Nancy." His face was closed and sorrowful and far away as if he saw memories that hurt him. "I've no lads to inherit. I've the house, and the beasts, and that's my life."

He waited.

Barrie clenched his hands, and the prayer inside him was so fierce that it must have shouted itself out through his head.

Da swallowed and looked up at the sky, as if he would read an answer there. Darkness was a brief moment away, but not yet come, and the sun was dying among the willows, flooding the water with colour. The wind whispered and three swans flew past, the still air thrilling to their wingbeats.

Mam looked up at the sky too; at the soft charcoal colour that would fade to midnight black, at one faraway yellow star that glimmered coldly, at the light glim that foreshadowed the rising moon, at the shapes of the trees and the hawking flitter of a solitary bat and Barrie thought that Mam too was praying.

A cow lowed in the byre, brought in because she was due to calve. Barrie thought of tomorrow when he would be back in the city, back among houses and crowding people, back in the squalid schoolroom with the sun shining in through the grimy curtainless windows and the hot smell of boys strong on the choking air, and he thought of the quiet byre and the calf standing beside its mother and thought of the little creature rustling the straw and saw himself bringing a bucket and teaching her to drink milk and the need to live here and work here was a yell inside him, was such intensity that it tore at his chest and at his stomach and his legs and he clenched his fists until his nails bit into his hands and he cried to the God in the chapel and the gods of the fields and the hills and the sky and the sun, and he thought he would die if Da did not answer soon. If they came to live here. . . .

Chapter 6

It was Mam who spoke, not Da, and Barrie did not understand what she said. They were being offered a chance, a chance to go back to all they knew, to live again, instead of existing. A chance to start again, a chance to get away, a chance to stop being Towhead, Goggles, Stupid, Taffy Welshman, a chance to be with beasts again and all the things he understood.

Please, please, please, be kind, God, just this once, I'll never ask anything again, he whispered.

49

It was useless.

Da was shaking his head and Mam was saying in an aching voice, "Does God exact day labour, light denied," and Barrie did not know what she was talking about. He only knew Da had been offered the chance of a lifetime and had turned it down and they were going back to the stifling stinking city and the rivers that had forgotten otters and kingfishers and fish, and they were going back to the teeming anthill existence and the misery of school, and the hard dirty pavements that were never clean, and there would never be a dog at his heels.

No dog.

No farm.

"Da," he said and his voice was pleading. "Da."

"No, boy bach," Da said. "We had to give it up once. I couldn't face it, not again. You never know, these days, what will happen. Nothing certain in life, boy, not in any life, not in farming life. Not like it used to be. I want you to have a chance."

It wasn't a chance, Barrie said, but he couldn't say it aloud. He couldn't talk to them, couldn't tell them he wanted nothing but the wind in the grass and the cattle lowing and the feel of them under his hands and the dog at his heel, never mind money, never mind all the things he would go without. They didn't matter. Who cared about having a car or watching the television, or making his fortune when there were living beasts asking to be cared for and all he ever wanted was here? It was no use even trying to tell them. They wouldn't understand. Da was sure he knew best, was doing right, and how did you tell your Da he was wrong and couldn't be more wrong? Barrie dragged after his parents, head down, fists clenched, wanting to hit out at a world so unbelievably hateful that he wished he were dead. The farmer watched them go, and went inside, but he had to come out again to call his dog. Terror had run after Barrie and the boy was kneeling beside the Labrador, his arms tight round its neck and its head was wet with tears.

Barrie blinked and wiped them away, furious with himself. He stood up and followed his parents and didn't look back, though he knew the man was holding the dog tightly by the collar and that it wanted to run after him. Life wasn't fair and Da was stupid and if there was a God he had forgotten them and he didn't want a better chance than his Da had. They could keep their rotten city jobs and their fancy degrees. Having a degree didn't make you know how to milk a cow or cure her of milk fever, or keep the ticks and maggots from her. It didn't tell you anything worth knowing. All he needed was a farm and cattle and a pig with a back to scratch.

Behind them the farmer whistled his dog and walked, back to the empty house. He knew how the boy felt. And he knew how the man felt. He thought of the boy's white face and the look on it, as if he had been given a prison sentence that would last a lifetime and maybe he had at that.

The farmer felt more lonely than ever before that night.

Barrie sat in the train and watched darkness swallow the land, and the thunderheads that had been building blotted out the sky and rain fell in sheets from an angry Heaven, slashing across the windows of the speeding train, washing away feeling until all that was left was dumb despair. Thunder drowned the train noise and lightning flashed over the light-patched towns but the storm outside was no worse than the storm inside the three of them as the train carried them back to the city.

Mam sat, huddled into herself, her face set and her lips tight and no words from her for she could not speak for tears. She stared into the rain and did not look at anyone. Da was angry and he snapped at Barrie almost every time he moved.

"Sit still, boy. You're like a dog with fleas," he said furiously. "Sitting there, fidgeting and glaring. It's no use boy and I don't want to talk."

But Barrie hadn't stirred and hadn't said a word and he hated Da and would hate him as long as he lived. There was nothing fair.

Just before they reached the station where they lived Da sighed heavily and looked across at Barrie.

"I'm sorry, boy, but there's the way it is and no other possible solution," he said, but Barrie only looked through him as if he did not exist and turned his head to watch the high brick walls and narrow backyards and the yellow lights that shone in rooms where the people lived in lonely despair, and never saw the flowers that bloomed in the country or the running water of a clean river, or a brown hare bounding.

He was not going to live in the city.

He was not going to have a good job, or go to college.

He was not going to school in the morning.

He was not going anywhere for Mam, or for Da, not ever again.

That night Barrie ran away.

Chapter 7

Barrie planned carefully. He was not going back to school. He was old enough to earn a living by himself and, somehow, he would find work in the country, as cowman on a farm. They were short of labour on all farms, and no one would ask questions, and it was no use staying with Mam and Da. They didn't understand. They didn't want to understand. Obstinate as old billygoats, they were, not seeing it was better to live a proper life doing things that were worth doing, and not doing something you hated, world without end amen.

He was not going to be trapped, not by the city streets, not by the city flats, not by the city jobs, not by the bribe of a good profession. There was only one profession for him, and that was farming. Or maybe he could go to Mike. But he knew that Mike would send him back. Maybe the farmer in the country would too, even if Barrie said his parents had given him the right to come. Too easy to check, with the telephone, and maybe Mam and Da would tell the police. Have to look different, he decided, no use being towhead any more.

Mam had some hair dye she used to blot out the grey. Been getting very grey lately, Mam had, getting old, like Da, Barrie thought. Too old to change, clinging to safety and a roof even if they did hate it and long for a better life. Wouldn't change. But he would.

When his parents slept he used the hair dye and stared at himself in the mirror, suddenly darkened, a chestnut brown that altered his whole appearance. No one could call him towhead now. He would find a farmer who had a dog and who wanted a cowman. Perhaps it would be a bitch and expecting pups and the farmer would let him choose his own pup and he would take it and name it Gelert and train it. The dog was a symbol of everything he longed for, and his own Gelert was dim since they came back from the country. The other dog had roused all the longing in him again. Not even Mike's dogs could assuage that. He longed to bring Rocha home, and have him for his own. It wasn't enough, just grooming him and walking him, every weekend. It only served to make the longing worse. It was like rubbing a cut to see if it were still sore and making it sorer still. It hurt horribly, but Barrie couldn't take the hurt any more, nor the teasing, nor the schoolroom, nor the city streets. He was stupid here, and would never be anything else but stupid, not wanting to live this way. He had to go and farm and maybe if he showed his parents how determined he was, Da would relent.

It would have to be a long way and Barrie hadn't enough money for the train. He counted it twice and hunted through his pockets but it made no difference. He would have to walk. Perhaps he could hitchhike. He would start by taking a bus to Victoria station and seeing how far he could travel from there, and then get out on to the road and maybe some driver would help him on his way. To the Sussex coast, perhaps, looking for a farm that was not too big and not too small. A big one would have only well trained men and no room for him; too small and they would not be able to pay a man at all. It had to be just right, and a lonely place and a man who wouldn't ask questions. It was a lot to expect.

He slipped out of the flat early in the morning, before anyone else was about. It was peaceful then and no boys pushing and yelling, no one to interfere with the lift so that for once he went from his own floor to the ground floor without it either stopping or suddenly shooting up again, or being left marooned because someone had switched off the power, and was out there, laughing, with a crazy sense of humour, not human at all.

The streets were wet with rain and gleaming in the lamp-light. Barrie pulled his duffel coat tightly about him. The wind was sharp. He looked back, up at the flat, at the closed curtains of the room where Mam and Da lay asleep. Maybe his Da wouldn't be so sorry to see him go, getting on so badly these days, they were, but Mam would mind. Lonely she'd be without him there and so much to do as well. Barrie helped her with the shopping and often cooked the meal when she was late at the shop, and ran messages for her and cleaned the family shoes and cleaned the bath, and washed the kitchen floor. Mam was busy all day and so tired when she came in, all she could do to drop in the big armchair and ease off her shoes and drink the tea he made her, and lie her head back as if it hurt her to open her eyes, and he hated watching her, and went to his room so that guilt would not needle, feeling he should do more and not knowing what.

"There's a terrible day I've had," she would say.

It wasn't easy, working with flowers, hands always wet and sore and red, and thorns on the roses, and the vases to clean and the window to dress and everything to be kept fresh and pretty. And her boss an old man who drank too much and never did his share and vanished at lunchtime and never back till four and her with all the work. And Da coming home tired too and late and working all hours. He'd never minded when a cow calved or the lambs were coming but this was different, this was working for other people, and never the satisfaction of working for yourself.

And never the satisfaction of seeing the small beasts running, little black faces and black patched knees, jumping and playing, two little lambs for the price of one, when the ewe bore twins, and the bottle feeding in the kitchen, and Da laughing as Mam held the little thing against her, and smiled down at it, and spoke softly. A long time since Mam spoke like that to anyone.

He ought to go back.

A dog slipped out of a doorway and stood and looked at Barrie. It was a black and white mongrel dog with a wicked little face and merry eyes and a wagging tail. It ran to Barrie and sniffed his leg, catching the memory of Terror from the day before, learning in one quick sniff that Barrie had been among cattle and had played with a dog, and had been abroad, far away from here. His clothes smelled of the country things and excitement. The dog frisked along, cocky, and Barrie remembered Terror vividly and knew he had to find work on a farm, any farm, so long as he was free again, among the beasts that he needed more than he needed food. He had invented Gelert and he knew that this was invention and now he had to make the invention come true. He had made the day before happen, had impelled his parents to go out and visit the farm, and it was the right farm. The right kind of farm, the right kind of man. Surely there was meaning there. There had to be meaning in life or there was no point in going on.

Just being born and living, often miserably, and dying. God didn't mean life to be like that, Barrie thought, with all the knowledge of his fourteen years. He had had a birthday last week. It was a landmark, a turning point, the beginning of adult life. He was, very nearly, a man. For all that, he had the appetite of a boy. He put his hands in his pockets and felt the few coins that rattled there. He had forgotten all about food. He was starving, and as soon as the shops opened he would find something to eat. He turned the corner and bumped straight into a policeman.

"You're up bright and early," the man said. "Delivering papers?"

Barrie nodded and hoped it didn't count as a lie, especially to a policeman, and he'd had his fingers crossed. Didn't like lies, Mam didn't, and she was always very angry if he told them. The policeman was bored and not particularly interested in delivery boys and Barrie looked harmless as well as scared. Funny colour hair, the policeman thought, looking down, noticing the patchiness, without quite realising why it looked odd. It never occurred to him that a boy might have dyed his hair. They'd tease him at school with those owl eyes and round glasses, the policeman thought, remembering his own schooldays not so many years before. He strolled on, intending to patrol the block of flats where Barrie lived. There was a wild lot of lads in that block. Always causing trouble, and the old people terrified of them and small wonder. He looked back. Barrie was staring hungrily into the newspaper shop, that also sold chocolates. It was open, ready for people going to catch the early morning trains. Barrie went inside to buy a bar of fruit and nut chocolate and stifle the pangs that were mounting each minute. The policeman walked on, satisfied.

Barrie came out again, and looked back, and hurried round the corner. The city was waking. Postmen, milkmen, policemen, the early morning lorries rattling to the market, the dustcart starting its round, big cab rattling, the clatter of bin lids. Shops waking too, and the lights coming on and the newsboys on bicycles. One of them, a big lout from Barrie's school, saw Barrie and failed to recognise him with his dark hair and looked away again. Barrie ate his chocolate and grinned to himself, delighted. No one would know him, now.

A moment later, not watching what he was doing, he felt the kerb beneath his feet, tripping him, and went flat, knocking off his glasses which fel in the road. A boy on a bicycle turned his head and looked at Barrie, and his bicycle wheel went over the glasses.

"You all right then?' he asked, and Barrie nodded, though he felt sick. He couldn't see properly at all without his glasses. No one had realised for a long time how shortsighted he was until the day he said there were no figures

56

on the clock on the other side of the room. He couldn't read the posters now, or the signposts, or the destination boards and time tables on the railway station. He couldn't even see the numbers on the buses or read where they were going. It was impossible. He had no money for new glasses, and how would he be able to see to do anything?

Anger surged in his throat. He almost turned back, but the memory of a dog's cold nose thrust into his hand spurred him on. He was going on, and he would find the farm they had visited again. The farmer was kind and would understand and would help him. If only Da would change his mind, but Da was obstinate and he did have a good job and the money coming in every week, not just when the lambs were sold, or the wool was sold, or the crops were sold, not dependent on market prices. By now Barrie was old enough to know that the farm had never paid, that they had always been in debt, the beasts could never be left without fodder, and there had been no other choice. Even so, he still hoped against hope. If he went into the church he was passing, maybe God would change Da's mind. It wasn't chapel, but perhaps this once God didn't mind, and did it matter where you said your prayers if it were the right prayers, whether it was Catholic or Protestant, Methodist or Baptist, Hindu or Mohammedan so long as you lived properly? There was only one God, the Church said so, and maybe if you lived in another place you called him by a different name. It was very confusing.

The church door was locked. Barrie sat on a tombstone and shivered, thinking of all the dead people lying around him. What sort of people had they been? Had they enjoyed life or gone from day to day always hoping for something better? Was that all there was, ever? He didn't know. He wished he were grown up and able to deal with problems. Surely grown-up problems were simpler, and you didn't care so much when you were old. Yet being grown up didn't seem to make much difference. Da was always worrying about something and Mam was too and always tired and hating the shop. Maybe Da could stay in his job and Barrie could earn enough for Mam to come and live in the country

57

too. She could help at the farm. Maybe if Mam came away too Da would find a proper place to live and they could have a dog. He worried and teased at his thoughts, getting mixed up, trying to sort out what he should do and where he should go and also getting hungrier and hungrier.

It was uncanny in the churchyard. Barrie shivered and walked back to the street. Daytime was waking it. Shops were rolling up their shutters, opening very early here because the women went to work. Men were sweeping the pavement. There was a smell of new bread, but the baker's door was closed. He turned into the yard and went towards the bakehouse and looked in through the door.

"Want some hot rolls, lad?" the baker asked and Barrie handed over some of his precious money and took the rolls, crusty outside and warm and moist inside and smelling like the farm had smelled in the old days under Tryfan. He thanked the baker and went out into the street and a brown dog came up to him, its eyes pleading for food. Barrie turned back to the churchyard and ate, sharing the bread, savouring the taste and watched the dog snatch at every crumb. Everyone in the world but he had a dog of their own. And some people didn't even take care of them. This one was starving, and its coat was uncared for and there was a forlorn look in its eyes. It ran off and left him and he stared at the ground, knowing there was no justice anywhere.

Behind him the church clock struck nine. School had begun and now he was totally committed. He had to go on. He could not face going back, ever.

Chapter 8

Barrie walked on thinking about dogs, thinking about Mike who had broken away from the usual pattern of living himself in order to work with the creatures he loved. People thought Mike was crazy, but he had what he wanted, the way he wanted it, and he was earning a very good living.

"There's always a way, if you want something badly enough," he said one day, watching Barrie put Rocha through his paces, knowing that Barrie would never, ever, fit into a city existence or a safe job, in office or bank. There would always be the yearning inside him.

David Griffiths said the same thing.

"No use doing something because you think you ought, boy, or because people will be disappointed in you if you don't do as they wish. Have to live your own life, boy, and its the only one you've got. Live it decent, is all, and if you can find out what you have to do and do it, that's all that matters. Not money, boy. Not possessions. That's not living, that's having things, and come disaster, or war, or famine, or any of the crises that can upset living for all of us, you have nothing left, boy. Only memory sour and sick in your throat and the knowledge you didn't try hard enough. Make your own road, boy, but make it on firm foundations, make it to last, no matter what."

Barrie remembered the conversation now and remembered too how he had looked up at the Growler and asked if he was doing what he wanted to do. The Growler nodded.

"I might have been a minister, but I wanted to teach more," he said. "Show other people the way to doing what they have to do, showing them the magic in the world, in the way the little creatures live. Lots of people think beasts aren't important, boy. Like saying God isn't important either. People don't know; no one has ever tried to teach them. I have to teach. You should know that, boy. You listen to what I say."

He listened. He'd always listen when people spoke of beasts. It was all that mattered. He was brilliant at biology, and good at figures and good at English. You needed words to talk and figures to work out milk yields and feed quantities and how much to pay for each. Nothing else was important.

Barrie walked on, through a world that was remote, not only in feeling. He couldn't see properly, couldn't see the names on the shop fronts or the faces of the people who passed him. The town was muted and softened and far away, and he trudged on, still hungry, both for food and for land, with the land hunger that he had only just recognised shouting at him through the mouths of all his ancestors, not only the Welsh ones, but the Danish great grandmother who had also been a farmer's daughter and who had been responsible for his fair colouring among all the dark Welsh folk. His Granda had often spoken of her, and his Granda had been towheaded too, and blue eyed, with fierce eyes that saw through a small boy, but that also loved him, and laughed at him and held him tightly and safe in strong arms. He missed Granda terribly when he died. The old man always had time to talk and time to listen, and time to tell stories of Wales and its great past and the Princess who had reigned over it, making it sound like a kingdom now enslaved, in thrall to strangers.

Barrie trudged on. He was coming to a part of the suburb that he hated even more than the flats where the old houses were coming down and stood gap-toothed and empty to the sky. There were only heaps of stones except at the corner where one shop still thrived. Even the bank was being demolished. As yet it stood sturdy on the outside, but rubble silted the empty doorway and there was light shining through the roof.

There was a sound from inside.

A small sound.

A puzzling sound.

A soft crying, a moan of misery that he could not identify.

He turned into the dark passage and it came again. It was a whimper, the noise made by a frightened puppy, a crying for its mother, or for human company, a dismal sound of utter loneliness. A sound that Barrie could not resist.

He went inside. Light gleamed from the hole in the roof, casting even darker shadows. The whimper came again and Barrie whistled. There was a faint soft bark.

He turned through a doorway, leading in the direction of the sound. It led to a long dark passage without a glimmer to break the darkness. He felt his way, guided by the soft whines. Some dog was trapped.

He was totally blind now. Nothing was left but feeling, guided by his hands, creeping along the wall. It had once been painted but now was greasy with dirt. It ended in blankness, where a wall had collapsed. The whimpers came from beyond.

Barrie began to move the rubble, working carefully lest it slipped and he was buried too. He remembered stories of mine accidents, and men who had died in the dark. He was as much in the dark as if he were down the pit and it was horrible. It pushed against him, solid, so that he felt overwhelmed and longed to run outside and see the bright day and the sun shining and the green of trees and the people alive out there, only a few yards from him. But the whines were excited now, a pathetic welcome from an animal knowing that help was here. Barrie could not leave him. He hesitated, wondering if he should go for adult help, but who would help him at this time of day when the traffic was rushing through and people were hurrying, skeltering off to work, and no one would have time for him.

He worked on, moving each brick carefully, feeling his way, making sure each was balanced and there was nothing loose to fall on him. There was dust everywhere, in his eyes and on his tongue, and all over his hands. Everything felt gritty and he must be filthy. No one would give him a lift now. He doubted if he could even go for the train, as he'd be so dirty. Everything was conspiring against him. Beyond him, the whining had risen to a crescendo. He worked on.

At last he had made a gap large enough to squeeze through. He could still see nothing. Only the terrifying darkness that hid the dog. The whines were nearer and he called to it and it barked again. He could picture it, there somewhere beyond him, perhaps caught by its collar. It would be Gelert, this time. It had to be Gelert and Mike would keep the dog for him and if he could have a dog, a dog of his own, he would go back to Mam and Da and try to live as they wanted. A dog would help. It would be something.

He climbed over fallen masonry and this time sensed that he was in a much bigger space. There was nothing in front of him. He must be in the main part of the bank. He moved forward incautiously, expecting solid floor to stretch in front of him and his foot slipped. He plunged headlong down a steep slope and fetched up with a thumping jar that left him breathless and shaken. He had bitten the inside of his lip and the running blood was sickly sour on his tongue and choking him as it flowed to the back of his mouth. He spat, and shook his head, trying to clear it. He looked up. Far above him a faint shine of light, mocking him.

A small body crept into his arms. He could not see the pup. He could only feel its warmth. It was thin and the ribs were harsh against his hand. An eager tongue licked his face. It might, it just might be an Alsatian. It had the right kind of head and the right sort of ears. "Gelert," he whispered, and the pup licked him again, and he could feel the wriggling body and the tail beating against his hand and the tongue licking his face, frantic with delight at having company, and, moreover, company that obviously wanted its presence. It crawled into his lap and lay, a dead weight across his arms, and he felt the strong paws that showed promise of growth and the tough little barrel-like body. It must have wriggled its way in here, perhaps chasing a rat or a cat, and fallen, and now what did they do?

There was half a roll left that Barrie had prudently put in his pocket against future hunger. He fed it to the pup who gulped it greedily and licked Barrie's face in grateful thanks. Barrie held the small body tightly. It was warm and it was comforting. There was no collar on it, no sign of ownership. It was a stray, it had been abandoned, perhaps it had been thrown here, deliberately. This was his dog, really his dog. No one was going to take it from him, not ever. He gripped the pup so tightly it yelped.

One thing was certain. They couldn't stay there, but they couldn't get out either. By the faint light Barrie could see they were in a hole in the ground that was over twelve feet deep. It must have been the old strongroom, underground. There was a slight slope upward but when he tried to climb, his feet slipped and he fell again, rolling hastily to avoid hurting the pup. The pup thought Barrie had invented a fine new game and cried out excitedly.

Barrie lay breathless, the wind knocked out of him again. He had no idea what to do next. Outside, the noise of traffic would drown every sound. He could hear it now, a steady relentless thrum, the buzz of passing cars, the squeal of brakes at the traffic lights on the next intersection, the whine of gears. Even if he yelled, who would hear, and would they think of coming in to the abandoned building to look? There was no sign that men had been working here recently. They had begun the demolition, or perhaps others had begun it, stripping the abandoned buildings of pipes and lead and tile and breaking glass. He must watch out for glass. So far he had been lucky and so had the pup. He felt every inch of its body and there was no sign of any broken bones. There were many sores and a gauntness that showed the pup was starved. His coat was thick with dust. He must have been running wild for days.

Barrie began to feel desperate. He might lie here for ever and no one find him. He thought of stories he had read of men dying in priestholes, of men dying in old caves and mine workings and only later were their skeletons found by those who came after. He could picture the builders coming weeks later to demolish the bank and finding his dead body, the dead pup clutched in his arms. Perhaps they would give Mam a medal, the R.S.P.C.A. because he'd tried to rescue the dog, even if he hadn't succeeded. In memory of Barrie Evans who died while attempting the gallant rescue of a trapped animal. Truly his was bravery beyond the call of duty. Ha ha, there's corny, Barry thought with contempt, knowing how absurd it was to think like that but he had to think of something and if he stopped and thought of being trapped and no one coming he would panic. Suppose no one found him, ever? Would Mam and Da be sorry? Or would they say good riddance, he always was a nuisance, might have known he would come to bad end and it served him right?

On the other hand he might be found too soon and taken home in ignominy to Mam and Da and the pup be taken from him. Or put on probation for running away and staying off school. Did they put you on probation for that? Barrie didn't know and clear as if she were beside him Barrie heard Mam say, "There's disgraced us, you have, Barrie. What ever made you do such a thing? There's daft you are, boy, and no more grown up than when we lived under Tryfan," and her voice would shake. Always remembering, Mam was. And he shouldn't have run away. God was punishing him. Didn't do, to do wrong, hell-fire waiting, like they said in chapel, the Minister's voice thundering out as if he had personally caught everyone sinning, there's wickedness abroad in the world today and lads who come to a bad end and men who take drink, and men who drink even on the Lord's Day, the Sabbath, and his finger would thrust out and point and the congregation stir uneasily. He had a fine ranting manner with him, had Mr. Pritchard, trained in Bangor and as Welsh as Barrie and his parents, coming to preach to all the Welshmen in the big city, daring temptation himself in the face of the command of the Lord, he had once said to Da when he came to call. Barrie had thought it funny, thinking of temptation coming for the Minister himself and wondering what kind it would be, drink or bad women, or something much worse. The Beast that stalked in Darkness, Mr. Pritchard called it, and his voice rolled out and rang in the rafters and everyone moved uneasily, especially the choirboys, and Barrie, in the choir, felt hot all over as he thought of all the things he had done wrong the week before, using bad language, and shouting at Mam and a lie about his schoolwork, not wanting Da to know he was bottom of the class in history again, not caring if Henry the Eighth had ninety-nine wives and beheaded all of them.

Now he was in darkness and maybe it was because he hadn't heeded the Minister, and what sort of Beast did stalk in the darkness? This thought was so terrifying that

Barrie held the dog against him and listened to the noises, and thought he could hear a beast's hooves thumping above him. In a moment, some horned horror with the face of a gargoyle in the nearby church graveyard would look down at him, and fourteen or not he was as scared as when he was five and had been caught in the big barn and the owl had come winging at his face from the rafters and Da had shouted and thrown his glove and grabbed Barrie and run. He could see the raking talons above him even now. She had young in the nest and would attack anyone who came near. Barrie never went near the old barn again when the owl was nesting, and even now, in his nightmares, he saw her body flying towards him and saw the cruel hook of her talons and the wild glare in her eyes.

Above him there were noises. A heavy breathing, and footsteps thundering. A giant from space? A Beast from Hell? A Fiend from the depths? Suppose this pit led to hell? There's daft, Barrie Evans, Barrie said contemptuously to himself but it didn't help. He lay clutching the pup, listening to the sounds above him.

Chapter 9

The sound came closer. Suppose it was some of the wild lads from the flats, also stayed off school? Barrie didn't know what to do. The pup settled the problem for him, and he realised it was younger than he had thought. It was very hungry. It had been down in the hole for two days and it was only half weaned. It grabbed Barrie's finger and began to suck, desperately hoping for milk. Barrie could not delay any longer. He had a sudden vision of one of the orphan lambs sucking at his finger, and food coming too late as they had been unable to reach the ewe, buried in the snow under Tryfan and the lamb too long without milk, its mother dead and it died too, even as it sucked. It was the first time Barrie had seen death, and even though it was long ago, the memory was vivid. He must attract attention. The trouble was, how?

If he shouted, would anyone hear? Then, also from the far past, came the memory of days spent on the mountain, long ago, of watching Da bring down the sheep and lambs, of Meg and Bob herding, working to a whistle and Da's voice echoing, down, Meg, down. To me then. Come, Bob, good lad, good lass, and when he was almost ready to come home, of Da's voice lifted in an exultant yodel that Mam could hear and put the lunch to cook so that it was ready and no time wasted. That would be in shearing time, Barrie thought. Da had taught him to yodel too, telling him how the men yodelled in Switzerland, calling to one another and how the sound carried. The first time he managed it, that had been memorable, with him and Da, a long way apart, yodelling to one another and the sound coming back from the mountains and the dogs barking and the barking echo in the valley too and everyone laughing. More laughter than there'd ever been since. If only he could remember how.

He filled his lungs.

"Yololololololeeeeeeiiiiiiii. Yololololololololeeeeeeiiiii."

The roof rang with the sound, the pup joined in with shrill whimpers and Barrie yodelled again.

"Yololololololololololeeeeeeiiiiiiiii."

The steps above stopped. There was a smothered exclamation and they turned and came towards him, closer and closer, thumping on the ground.

"Don't come close!" Barrie yelled, suddenly anxious. "There's a big hole in the floor. I'm at the bottom and I can't get out."

The footsteps stopped. A voice spoke. It was a man's voice, and Barrie breathed a deep sigh of relief.

"OK, son," a voice said. "I'll go and get help. I haven't a light. Didn't mean to come in here but thought I heard a dog whine."

"You did," Barrie said. "He was here first and I tried to get him."

"Not broken anything?" The man asked. "Don't need an ambulance."

"I'm all right," Barrie said. "The pup's starving."

The pup continued to suck his thumb. Barrie held it close, treasuring it, feeling the breath lift its ribs, feeling the fur and the warmth, feeling the need for it, and the knowledge that he was caring for it, helping it, and could bring it food and life. The footsteps died away.

Time had ceased. He had no idea how long he had been down the hole, how long ago now school had started, whether Mam and Da would have gone off to work without looking to see if he was up. If they were late they left him to get his own breakfast and see to himself. They both left home far earlier than he did. They wouldn't miss him till teatime, especially as sometimes in summer he got up extra early and went to walk in the Park, pretending he was back in the country again, and that any moment now, the dogs would come and he could go with them to fetch the cattle in for milking. It was a desperate hunger, and it was worse now that he had glimpsed farm life again the day before. He thought of the sleek Jersey cattle. They would be browsing in the fields, and the lorry would be turning in at the farm gate and taking the churns of rich milk and the farmer would be working about the place chasing time through the day, all alone, when Da and he might have been helping.

He would still have to go to school, for two years at least, but it would be a country school where everyone knew the importance of crops and cattle and talked his kind of talk and it would be a place where a dog could run free and be trained and taught and it was close enough to Mike for him to take his dog and have Mike help him teach it. They'd go in for obedience trials like Mike did and go to a club and the fat rosettes would be pinned on the dresser, rosettes to show how well they had done, he and Gelert. Gelert would be easy to train and he knew how to start. He'd helped with Mike's new pup, little Zea, who was not much bigger than this pup and would already sit and walk to heel for Barrie. There was achievement.

Meanwhile time was passing and he was hungry and maybe the man didn't intend to come back, or had been run over on the way to get help. Always road accidents on that bit of road where it narrowed and the cars couldn't see what was coming round the bend and people crossed to get to the chip shop, not looking, thinking only of food, and suddenly saliva was flooding Barrie's mouth, mixing with the blood still running from his cut lip, as he thought of golden fish, the batter crisp and crunchy and the fish white and flaking away and hot inside and yellow-brown chips, the way Mam cooked them, tasting of manna, food for the gods themselves, food fit for Eden, food that he would exchange almost anything in the world for. Except the pup. He swallowed.

There were heavy footsteps again, and the sound of bricks being shifted. A light shone downwards, blinding him, so that he put his hands over his eyes and screwed them up tight, hurting with the glare. The pup whined too and hid its head under Barrie's arm, shutting out the intrusive stab of light. "We'll have you out of there in no time. They're bringing a ladder. Been down there long?"

The man shone his torch on his own face. The voice was different. This was a policeman. Barrie saw the flat peaked cap. His escapade was over. He would have to go back now. There would be no dog. No farm. Only the city and the people and the dark dirty streets as the trap closed, world without end, amen. He had earned hell-fire too and Chapel next Sunday would an uncomfortable place indeed. He only hoped Mam and Da didn't realise that he had run off and thought he had made a detour on the way to school and been caught going for the dog. But he was miles from school, or the Park.

The torch shone comfortingly into the hole, away from Barrie's face. It shone on bricks and rubble. It shone on Barrie's dusty legs and a hole in his trouser knee and there would be trouble over that. It shone on the pup. Scraggy, scrawny, dirty, but black and tan under the dust with an Alsatian head and brown warm eyes, and an Alsatian body and strong good paws and a good long tail, all Alsatian, every scrap of him. The tail was moving happily, and the dog couldn't be closer to the boy if he tried. Barrie longed to get him out and clean him up.

"Gelert," he whispered, and the pup wagged his tail.

"They won't be long," the policeman said comfortingly. He was squatting at the edge of the hole, directing the beam of the torch, knowing that a human presence would help. "How did you get down there, for Heaven's sake?"

"I was out for a walk, early, before going to school," Barrie said and his fingers were crossed and he hoped God would forgive him. Didn't want more trouble than he could help, not now, with Da to persuade to let him keep the dog, to let him board it with Mike, to give him chance to have a creature of his own to love. The Minister himself had said only last week that Shakespeare knew what he was talking about when he said, "There's a divinity that shapes our ends." Everything that happens to you is meant, has a reason, the Minister had gone on. Not always an obvious reason. God means you to use your brains, work it out. If you read it right it leads on to Glorious Destiny and if you read it wrong it leads on to Hell-fire and Damnation. So this was meant. All of it. His escapade and his finding of the pup. He had saved its life. It might have died down there in the dark alone. God had led his footsteps and even Da couldn't argue with God. It had been an impressive sermon. Barrie listened to the voice thundering, with fascination; it was a wonderful voice, as good as any actor's, every word fraught with meaning, the tone almost like singing. The Minister could sing. His voice led the choir and soared to the roof and up and up, Mam said, to the angels, who would have to listen.

Sometimes at the Christmas concert that they gave for the old people at the Darby and Joan club the Minister sang the old songs of Wales, songs like "All Through the Night", and then the old people had a request time and he sang other songs, the "Songs of the Isles", and "Oh No John", and the "Road to Mandalay", and once he led them all in a rousing chorus of "Bobby Shaftoe", and once he had recited a Welsh lay that had fascinated Barrie. He felt safe now the light was shining and said the words aloud, not knowing what else to say.

> "The mountain sheep are sweeter,
> But the valley sheep are fatter.
> We therefore deem it meeter,
> To carry off the latter.
> Ednyfed, King of Dyfed,
> His head was borne before us.
> His wine and beasts supplied our feasts,
> His overthrow our chorus."

There's daft he was, but rescue was a long time coming.

"You're Welsh," the policeman said. All Barrie's lilt had come back.

"Yes," Barrie said.

"Great singers, the Welsh," the policeman said. "Can you sing, boy?"

"Yes," Barrie said again.

"Then we'll both sing. Pass the time away. I'm in the police choir and we have a concert soon. What shall we sing?"

There's daft, Barrie thought again lying at the bottom of a hole in a half demolished bank with a dog in my arms and singing with a policeman. He wanted to laugh. He also wanted food, and so did the pup.

"They have to go and get ladders," the policeman said. "Maybe get the firemen. I don't know. What about singing 'Jerusalem'? But not too loud, lest the bricks decided to settle. Don't want the walls of Jericho here."

Softly the words sounded on the air.

> "Bring me my bow of burning gold,
> Bring me my arrows of desire.
> Bring me my spear, O clouds, unfold.
> Bring me my chariot of fire."

And there, plain as plain in his head, was sunset red on Tryfan and the sky ablaze from end to end and the ridged streamers of scarlet threading through the black and himself small again and in the little chapel in the valley watch-

70

ing the sun die and the night gobble up the day and the voices sing the same song as he was singing now, for old Mrs. Mary Davids who was English but had lived in the valley all of her married life, and her father a preacher in a little church on the wide moors beyond Buxton. Sometimes too Da preached, as a lay preacher. He had once preached in the prison and come back grim faced and not spoken to anyone all evening, and at bedtime Barrie had heard him say through the wall:

"Those great iron doors clanging shut behind you, girl. There's terrible. Enough to keep a man on the straight and narrow for ever, I should have thought. But there's wickedness, outside."

Barrie thought of the iron doors clanging shut and shivered. Enough to keep him on the straight and narrow for ever. He was imprisoned by the city but he could get out and take a train and see the wide fields and the sky above him. To be shut in, in a cell, with high walls and wire and dogs guarding, and the alarm bell ringing if a man broke out, that was terrible, and only hellfire could be worse. He wished the policeman would sing again, or talk again. Lying there thinking was far from pleasant, but what did you talk about, down at the bottom of a stupid old hole, with a pup in your arms waiting for a ladder? Nice day, mister. There's daft and he didn't know if it was raining or not.

"I should think the ladder's fallen down the Treacle Mine," the policeman said.

"The Treacle Mine?"

The policeman laughed.

"I've got two kids who like treacle and the little one thought it came out of a mine. So whenever anything happens at home we can't explain, we tell him it's fallen down his treacle mine. Gets to be a habit," the policeman said. "How old are you, son?"

"Fourteen," Barrie said, though he didn't feel fourteen at the moment. Did you ever feel as old as you were, he wondered. Mam often said she felt twenty again, or two hundred today, all depending, and Da didn't act old, though

71

he must be old, well over forty by now, nearly half a century, alive when there were horses and carts, not many, going out of fashion, but not everyone with old lorries, Da said. More peaceful then. Did people always want to go back, afraid of change, Barrie wondered suddenly. Even he wanted to go back, but not because he didn't like change. He wanted to farm the new way, big herds of cattle and wonderful buildings. He never would. You needed money for everything, these days. Not fair, some people had it and others didn't and where was that old ladder, he'd go daft, waiting, and he'd sing silly songs like Crazy Joe, the old tramp who sold matches down by the railway bridge and made up funny little rhymes and shouted them at people who wouldn't buy his matches. Not nice rhymes, either. Always being warned off was Crazy Joe, and Brett and his friends used to go and tease him and yell daft things at him and he'd yell back and chase them, shouting his angry doggerel. They took care to keep well out of reach, scared of him, Barrie thought with sudden insight. He'd managed to sort some funny old things out, lying here in the hole, nothing to do but think, not able to go anywhere.

Never time to think, ordinarily, or maybe he didn't really want to try. Better to shut his eyes to some things. Better to think Da and Mam were against him than to know they were as unhappy as he, trapped by the need to live, to earn money, the need perhaps to look after him. Doing it all for him and he didn't even want it. There's daft, life was. Nothing like the way it had been in the valley when he was small and safe, and didn't know about the world outside. Was this growing up? Knowing nothing was safe, ever, that everything changed, that you had to adapt, to survive. Survival of the fittest, the Growler often talked about it. What was fittest in the world today? To fight? To make bombs? To riot?

"Penny for them, boy," the policeman said, easing his position. Help was a long time coming.

Barrie tried to collect his wits.

"Just wondering," he said at last, unable to say any of it to a stranger or even to Mam and Da, or even to the

Growler. Not easy ever to think about important things.

There were voices outside. Help had come at last, and Barrie was saved from the need to try and explain his thoughts.

Chapter 10

Within minutes there was hustle and bustle all about him. A searchlight was set up beside the policeman, blazing down into the hole with such brilliance that neither Barrie nor the pup could see. When his eyes adjusted Barrie saw rough concrete walls, rough floor, dirt and dust. He was covered with filth and so was the pup. He had felt the grit in its fur but not realised it was so bad. He hugged it tighter.

A ladder was lowered into the hole, and one of the firemen climbed down and took the dog. Barrie did not want to let go.

"He's a stray," he said. "He's mine, now."

The fireman looked down at Barrie's anxious face.

"I'll give him back to you," he promised. "Up you go. I'll be right behind. Not hurt, are you?"

Barrie shook his head. He was bruised and sore but not really hurt. The worst part was being unable to see properly, but he could feel. He gripped the rungs with his hands and climbed up, and stood thankfully on the ground beside the policeman. The fireman came after him and handed him the pup and Barrie grabbed it and held it close, his hands gentle.

He blinked again when he walked outside. The day was bright, sun shining on the street, the bustle of morning filling the pavement with people, and with noisy cars racing to unknown destinations on the busy roads. It was not nearly so late as he had thought. Sound had vanished, deep under the road, in the dark.

He looked down at himself, at his torn and filthy clothes, at his cut and bleeding hands, at his grazed knees, and at the pup, lying close against him, snuggling up to the first comfort that it had known in its brief life. He saw it properly for the first time, looked at it with total horror and disbelief and sickness choked him.

"There's cruel," he said furiously.

The policeman looked down. There was a wire twisted round the pup's neck, bitten deep into the skin, so deep that Barrie had not felt it under the fur. There were half healed cuts all over the small body, and the ribs stood out, skeleton sharp. It was a sorry object, but for all that its tail waved and it licked Barrie's hand.

"Cruel indeed," the policeman agreed, his voice angry. He took the pup in gentle hands, but could do nothing about the wire around its throat. "We must get him to the vet. Luckily there are dog handlers at our station and the vet should be there this morning, come to look at one of our dogs. He was due at eleven, and it's just about that now. Someone tried to get rid of that pup, so if you want it you can keep it and no one will be claiming it. If they do, they'll be in trouble, as I'm going to report it to the R.S.P.C.A. and they'd have a good case. Now, boy, anyone waiting for you at home?"

Barrie shook his head.

"Mam and Da both go out to work," he said. "Nobody at all will be there till my Mam comes back at teatime."

"We'll go to the station and clean you up," the policeman said. "Hungry?" He knew about boys.

Barrie nodded.

"But the pup's hungrier," he said.

The policeman laughed. Barrie sat in the back of the police car, looking out at the streets, the pup safe in his arms again.

"You're keeping the pup," the policeman said.

Barrie nodded. He didn't know how, but he was. Mike would take it for him, and he'd work for Mike all hours at the weekend to earn its keep. He'd clean cars and find a paper round. He could surely earn enough for its food.

"It's going to cost you in vet bills, son. Unless you can get it to Victoria, to the Blue Cross, and they'd help you with it, especially after such treatment. All the same, you'll probably need a vet sometime for it. And Alsatians eat a lot. That's probably why it got thrown out. Someone bought the bitch for his kids and it had pups and he found it a more expensive proposition than he expected. People are impossible."

Barrie looked down. The soft coat was matted with dirt, and the pup was a mess, but he hadn't been misled. He knew enough now from Mike to recognise breeding when he saw it and this pup already showed its ancestry. Perhaps Mike would show it for him and they'd win rosettes for its breeding as well as its obedience. Perhaps it would sire wonderful puppies and make him a fortune and he could buy his farm. The pup licked Barrie's wrist. He wanted Barrie as badly as the boy wanted him.

There was interest and friendliness at the police station. One of the dog handlers came in, and took Barrie out to the kennels at the back, where the vet was already looking over a dog with a badly cut paw, cut on glass left by vandals outside a telephone kiosk. The kennelman, small and dark, with a quiet manner and a keen eye, drew his breath in sharply when he saw the pup.

"I'd like to kill whoever did that," he said.

He took the pup from Barrie, and stood it on the table in the feed room, and took a bowl of water and a damp cloth and began to wipe the dust away from the coat. Barrie held it, and it stood, patient, surprisingly quiet.

"Go and wash yourself while the vet looks him over, son," the kennelman said gently.

Barrie looked at the pup. It looked dreadful and was so quiet that a new fear knifed into him and he clenched his fists.

"He won't put him to sleep?" Not now, not when I found him, not when I found my own dog. No. He stared up at the kennelman, whose face was blurred. If only he had his glasses.

"Don't you fret," the man said, knowing how Barrie

felt, a man who thought dogs important, a man who spent his life at the kennels helping nurse them when they were sick, looking after them when they were well, when they came in to be cared for while their handler went on holiday. Dogs were his life, as they were Mike's life too.

Barrie went to wash. A doctor had come to the police station and he bathed Barrie's cuts and dressed them, and went away again, and Barrie washed and combed his hair with his fingers and turned blindly and bumped into the wall before he found the towel.

"I lost my glasses," he explained to the policeman who had found him, and who had come to look for him. "It's no use going to school. I need a new pair. I can't see an old thing without them. I fell over and they got broken this morning."

"You can see to eat," the policeman said. "I've not had my breakfast yet. I was on the way to get it when the man at the corner shop found you. He came to investigate because he thought he heard the pup crying. He hadn't been able to go before as he was too busy in the shop. Come on. We'll feed the pup as soon as the vet's seen him. He'll be all right with Bill. Best kennelman we ever had. He knows more about dogs than most vets have forgotten in a lifetime."

Barrie ate an enormous helping of bacon and egg and sausage and tomato and fried potatoes, given him by a grinning canteen assistant who guessed he had hollow legs and who knew boys as she had two teenage sons of her own. He wanted to go back to the pup, and as soon as they had finished, the policeman took him outside again, and across the yard and Barrie ran into the shed, afraid again, wondering if the vet had had to put the pup to sleep. The wire had cut so deep.

But the pup was wagging his tail and Bill had put a bandage round his neck and the vet was washing his hands.

"I'll give you a diet sheet for him," he said. "He's about twelve weeks old, I should think, but he's in appalling shape. You'll have your work cut out to get him straight. I've had a whole litter like this, got rid of in different places, in the last two days. This chap was lucky. The rest are dead."

The vet stroked the pup.

"I don't much like people," he commented, and went away, a small and very angry man who spent his life clearing up mistakes made by carelessness and ignorance and stupidity.

Bill had poured some milk into a saucer, and mixed it with puppy meal. The pup was eating as if he had never seen food before in his life.

"You need special baby milk for him," Bill said. "Cow's milk won't do. And this stuff, which is for pups. And vitamin tablets, to make up for what he's missed in the last weeks. It looks as if his mother probably didn't have enough milk for the pups. He didn't get like that in a couple of days."

Barrie knelt on the floor and watched the pup eat. This was his pup. He shut his mind against refusal. It had to be his pup. This was meant, just as the Minister said. There had to be sense in the chance encounter. There had to be meaning to everything that happened, to the farm yesterday, which made him run away, and if he hadn't run away he wouldn't have found the pup. Maybe he wasn't meant to farm, ever, but was meant to have the pup. He was meant to fall into the hole, just when the pup was down there. It was no use praying though. Prayers didn't get answered. Things happened or they didn't happen and maybe this was the start after all.

The policeman had a son of his own and knew a lot about boys. He was off duty, but was in no hurry. He began to talk to Barrie, not probing, not asking, just an odd question here and there, and he was an easy man to talk to, and he listened, so that suddenly Barrie was telling him and Bill all the things that had been hidden for a long time, telling him about the farm and the mountains and yodelling with Da and how he came to remember, and about the Sunday visit to the country and the farmer who needed help and how Da was working for the Post Office, and how Mam went out to work and grew flowers on her windowsill and how they went to the Park whenever there was time, and

77

about Mike and his dogs, The policeman knew Mike, it seemed. He was famous in the Alsatian world and often found suitable dogs for the police handlers, knowing the kind they needed, with a steady temperament, easy to train, but fierce when asked to be, perhaps a bit mean looking, but never mean by nature. It made it even easier to talk to the policeman, him knowing Mike.

Made it easy to tell him about his imaginary dog, Gelert, and how he'd wanted one so badly he'd gone to the class and pretended he was bringing it to train, and how he was going to keep this one and call him Gelert, no matter what. He ended on a forlorn note, because there were too many ifs. Da might refuse outright. Mike might not have kennel space. He might not, even though he tried, be able to earn enough money for its food. It would cost an awful lot with special milk and vitamins and puppy food, and it could eat too. It had finished everything on the plate and had come to Barrie and was leaning against his knee, looking up, and Barrie wanted the dog more than he had ever wanted anything in his life.

"I don't want any of their old jobs," he said desperately, "I want to go and work on a farm and one day go back to the mountains, away from the flat lands. I want room to keep a dog. It's no life at all, in a city."

No life at all without trees and the sky wide above and the ground clean and rainwashed and smelling of damp soil and wet grass and of Maysmell in summer, and flower-smells, wild plants, wild garlic overpowering, bluebells in summer woods, and honeysuckle in the hedges tangled with the wild rose, with the low of cattle and the baa of sheep and baby creatures all about, and his dogs running. The pup pawed at Barrie's knee and whimpered and Barrie came sharply back to the present and picked it up and held it tightly, defying the whole world to take it from him.

The policeman looked at the kennelman as Barrie went outside.

"He's young for his age," the kennelman said. "Nice to see, not wanting to grow up too soon, learning bad habits, smoking and drinking and aping men who ought to know better."

"He's going to be hurt, all his life," the policeman said. "I only hope it doesn't start right now. That dog could make all the difference to him. It's a chancy age."

"It's one hell of an age," the kennelman said, remembering from a long way back all the injustices of being fourteen and all the miseries, and some of the joys too.

"The pup will have to be house trained," the policeman said in the car on the way back to the flat. Barrie said nothing. Obstacles were rising every minute. They stopped off at the optician to order new glasses, and there would be another expense and Mam complaining bitterly again. He was always needing new glasses. Sometimes he broke them but more often one of the lads at school snatched at them and once Brett had trodden on them, and laughed while he did it.

Reality was intervening. Barrie's face was tight, and he shied away from his thoughts, knowing perfectly well that he had been pipe dreaming again and that nothing would change. Everything would be the same, and today go on as yesterday, and all that lay ahead was an office job or a factory job, or a teaching job, and a life indoors and money coming in each week and a narrow little house or a flat looking across the road at other houses and other flats, and the country lying there as out of reach as Heaven, and far more desirable. Rather be a tramp and never work at all, Barrie thought.

But the flat was empty still and Barrie did not want Mam called away from work, as she would worry. The policeman took Barrie and his pup back to his own home, and his wife fed both of them. Da and Mam must have gone out without missing him and maybe they would never need to know he had run away. After lunch he went home, the pup tucked under his coat, and sneaked up the stairs, lest he shared the lift and the pup whimpered and someone reported him.

No one was in.

He sat in his room, staring out of the window at the world

below. It was dwarfed to insignificance. Tiny cars crawled aimlessly, tiny people hurried through the streets, a dog ran across the raw earth where grass could not fight against the encroaching feet that trampled it flat and destroyed every blade. Pollarded trees, reduced to total ugliness, lined the edge of the bare ground. A tattered pigeon preened itself on the window ledge. The pup slept on Barrie's knee, and he waited with dread for his mother to come home. He had changed his clothes. His ruined trousers were on the window seat.

Her key sounded in the door. He should have got the tea, but he had not moved. He couldn't move. The pup might make a pool or worse if he put it down. He did not want to go out and face his Mam.

"Barrie?"

"I'm here, Mam."

"Are you ill?" She opened the door. "Barrie, there's a mess your clothes are in. Aren't you old enough to look after them properly? Dye, and where did that come from, indeed? What are you doing with it here?"

But already Mam's eyes were looking at it with pity, seeing how small it was and how hurt it was and it was wagging its tail, hopefully, tentatively, asking her to let it stay, to take it in, to keep it. Barrie watched her face soften and a small hope began to flutter.

"I found it down a hole. That's how I got so dirty," Barrie said.

Mam was looking at the pup's body, at the cuts and sores and the bandage, now bloodied, that was wound round its throat. She knew how Barrie felt. She knew how she felt. She took the small animal from him and held it for a moment and Barrie handed her the tube of ointment that the kennelman had given him. She took it and began to dress the sores, soothing each injury with gentle hands, her face absorbed. Barrie said nothing.

When his father came home he was sitting on the window seat. The pup lay beside him, its head on his knees, its eyes looking up at him. It had come home, and it was relaxed and happy and totally at ease. There was food waiting on the table, and Mam silent, not looking at his Da, was serving it on to their plates.

Da looked at Barrie. He looked at the pup. Barrie did not need words. All his longing was in his eyes. His mother moved the plates across to their places at the table, and took a plate of puppy meal and milk, which the kennelman had also provided, and set it on a newspaper on the floor. The pup started to eat.

Barrie watched his Da's face, saw his Da's eyes look at the pup's bruised body, watching the pup eat and finish and walk across the room and look up at the man, as if it wished to show affection, but feared a blow. Da moved his hand to stroke the pup and it crouched flat, ears back, and whimpered, cowering away.

"Da," Barrie whispered.

But his Da was on the ground, his face momentarily angry, and then tender, and his hands reached out to the pup, reassuring. He picked it up and spoke softly and stroked the small head, and the pup wriggled and reached up and licked Da's face.

"It's like Nell, the pup we had when we were first married, remember, girl?" Da said.

The pup settled itself in Da's arms, and rested its head against Da's broad shoulder.

"There's trusting," Mam said.

Da looked at Barrie and cleared his throat.

"I thought it over," he said. "I thought all day. The farmer rang me, at work, first thing this morning. I thought of the cattle and the milk coming warm into the pails, and the boy . . ."

Da paused and Barrie waited, holding his breath.

"I telephoned," Da said. "On the way home. We can go as soon as we like. There's a flat we can have, part of the farmhouse, he doesn't need all those rooms, and Mam can help with the house and the cattle, and maybe sometime we can go into partnership, he and I. He has no sons. There's a school for the boy. We better go soon, girl, maybe send Barrie down at once. Can't keep the pup here."

There was no sound in the room. Only the tick of the

clock. Only Barrie's breathing, coming so fast it hurt, only the murmur of Barrie's fears, telling him he couldn't have heard right, it couldn't be true. But it was true and Mam was standing there crying into the potatoes and Da was grinning an embarrassed grin and Barrie was unable to say a word though inside him he was yelling with delight. It was too good to happen. It couldn't be true.

"The pup's just like Nell," Da said. "Better go and phone the farmer yourself, boy, and ask if you can come tonight and bring him with you. Can't have him here. And take him outside. But be careful. Can't put a collar on that sore neck."

But the pup didn't want to leave Barrie's side. It stayed close, in the playground, where he walked it, beside him in the phone box, ringing the number his Da had given him, waiting for the man at the other end, spilling out the story of the pup he had found and could he come now and could he bring it and could he keep it, the words tumbling over themselves till the farmer laughed and said, "Whoa, lad, steady, come at once, of course," and Barrie rang off and danced into the evening and overhead the pigeons crooned and their coos were triumphant.

The starlings poured across the sky, darkening it, their voices defying the traffic. Barrie bent and lifted the pup, and stood, looking up. Streamers raced across the sunset, scarlet and black, long trailing banners, memories of Tryfan, promises of the future.

Barrie lifted his head. He was dwarfed by the buildings, but his voice drowned the starlings' noise as the excitement built inside him and spilled over and could not be stilled and a passing police car stopped and the policeman grinned as he got out and went upstairs to see Barrie's parents. He suspected there was now no need. All the way up in the lift the sound echoed, hurling itself against the high towers that shot into the sky.

"Yolololololoeeeeiiiiiiii. Yolololololoeeeeiiiiiiii."

Da leaned out of the window and joined in and Barrie answered him and the pup whined and the windows flew open and faces looked out astounded as the yodels sang on the air and echoed and re-echoed.

But Barrie did not care.

"Yololololoeeiiii. Yololololoeeiii."

The sound rose to the distant stars and at the station the train waited, and the farmer met him and tomorrow Mam would come and Da would come and Gelert slept beside him, but Barrie could not sleep.

He listened to the cattle lowing in the stalls, and the owl-calls harrowing the night. He watched the moon silver the trees and shine across the bed.

He lifted the pup and it curled against him, and flung one paw across Barrie's cheek.

They had both come home.

THE END

THE GREAT LAD

It had been a wicked day. Snow lay deep in crack and crevice and gully, drifted against the drystone walls, and hid the shape of the land beneath it. A wind whipped across the steeps, whining as it came, and the trees were heavy and doom laden, branches cracking under the sullen weight.

The dog had been uneasy all day. Restless as they quartered the ground, digging out the ewes, and trying to guide them back to the farm through snow that came tail high, so that the beasts plunged miserably, each step a struggle.

He could not tell his master his fears. The snowfilled sky lay dark and leaden, sulphur yellow on the far horizon, eerie with light that made the dog shiver. The hill grumbled to itself, too softly for the shepherd to hear, but loud enough to panic the sheep and make the dog unbiddable.

Twice he crouched and whined, refusing to move on, and the man shouted at him, hating the weather and annoyed that his dog should choose such a day to play him up. He wanted to get back to the farmhouse, to scalding tea and a blazing fire. He cursed the sheep.

Once he used his crook to drag a beast down from a rocky plateau where it stood stupefied, never having seen such weather before in its short life. Once he had to use it to help the dog out of a drift that covered a deep gully, and into which the animal plunged with a yelp of terror.

A moment later, the dog was clear. The man used his crook to judge the depth of the snow, and found a way to the other side, but before he reached it the hill shuddered, and a weight of snow and rock and earth came tumbling from the heights, gathering momentum in a tide that came faster and faster, straight for the man.

The dog barked and ran. The man followed, clumsy in his thick clothing. He missed the main tide, but a rock struck his shoulder, and another, hurling itself downwards, pinned his arm as he fell. Try as he would, he could not move, but lay helpless as an insect pinned on a collector's board.

He whistled the dog and Moss came doubtfully, tail moving slowly, not in greeting, but in bewilderment. He was too young to have seen snow before, and he was well drilled. He knew he must never move without his master's command.

Now Wyn Jones cursed the gruelling training he had given the dog. Training that ensured that if told to sit he would sit for two days if not given a counter order, training that ensured he would watch other dogs herd sheep, and never interfere. Training that ensured he would rely on his master's brains and never on his own.

"Home, lad," the shepherd said.

He could think of no other command. If the dog came alone they would come out and look for him. If it did not snow they might be able to follow his tracks. If it did snow . . . Wyn Jones closed his eyes and prayed to his Maker, sweat darkening his skin in spite of the cold that seeped through his clothes and the damp that soaked him.

The dog was puzzled. "Home" was a command for unruly pups, not for a grown dog out with his master on the hill. He crept forward, whining.

"Home, you fool."

The voice was testy, but not yet a shout. The dog looked at the sheep, grey against the dazzling white, huddled in misery, woolly fleeces close packed, as they waited patiently for someone to herd them.

Wyn Jones cursed to himself, for one of the ewes was due to lamb and any lamb born in the snow and the cold was doomed unless he could get them to safety.

"Home, dog," he yelled, with all the strength he could muster, and watched anxiously as Moss's tail went between his legs, and crouching, hangdog, punished unknowingly, he turned away.

But Moss could still not believe his ears. There was work to be done, and his master had no right to lie in the snow. He ran back and tried to dig at the rock that held him prisoner. Jones sighed. The poor beast was trying his best, but help must come from men.

"No," he said sharply, and the dog backed away, head on one side, ears half-cocked, puzzled.

"Home!" the shepherd roared.

This time the dog started, but kept looking back, eyes anxious, as if hoping to see his master stand and follow him. Soon, persuaded that this was not going to happen, he gave his whole mind to following the trail back to the farm.

He knew the way, by scent and sight, and by the feel of the ground, but scent was masked, landmarks had vanished, and the unbroken hummocked snow lay all around him. He plunged and floundered, afraid of the quietness, of the absence of birds, and the dimming light, and the sultry glow in the sky.

Much was hidden because he was small. Each crest was a mountain, to be traversed with difficulty. Once he fell into a small drift and struggled out again, panting. Once he dropped to the ground to rest, but the command given him was too powerful. His duty was to obey, and he had to go home.

The shepherd, lying where he had fallen, wiped tears of cold away from his eyes with gloved fingers, and looked at the sheep. They stood listlessly, heads hanging, tails into the wind. When he moved one of them turned towards him, and perhaps seeking shelter under the lee of the snow that partly covered him, came and stood beside him.

The other sheep followed, breaking the wind, unknowing that their coming offered the shepherd a longer grip on life. He pulled at the nearest fleece, and the ewe lay in the snow against him, the presence of the familiar man giving her comfort. He pushed his hands into the rank smelling wool, and dozed, dreaming uneasily of hot coffee and steak and kidney pudding, rich with warm gravy, and the warmth and comfort of the farmyard. Each waking was a small agony.

The sheepdog was half way home. The wind caused his eyes to water, stung his eyeballs, and froze his muzzle so that there was ice clinging to the fur around his jaws.

He hungered more for men than for food. Men who encouraged him and brought him comfort and gave him warmth. He could not bear the dismal landscape where nothing moved, and he was too low on the ground to see the far away plume of welcoming smoke from the farm-house chimneys.

He struck the track, worn by the passing of sheep and men, and ran more jauntily, the freer movement bringing warmth. When he paused, weary, his breath plumed on the air and he shook his head, not liking this sudden surprising manifestation of something he could not understand.

The track ended, as the men had turned away to a farm lower down the valley. His own, the sheep still on the hill, caught by the sudden early unseasonable November snow-fall, lay trapped and white, the only path cleared round the yard so that the cows could be brought for milking and pigs and chickens fed.

The dog was almost home when the blizzard struck, coming without, for him, any warning. One moment he was plunging, able to see, through hardpacked snow in which were the tracks of fox and stoat and weasel, and of foraging birds. The next, blindness came on him as the great flakes swirled on the wind and fell on eyes and muzzle, on shoulder and back, and on his head and neck, so that he shook himself repeatedly and then sat in the clammy snow using first one paw and then another to try and clear away the clinging uncanny stuff that prevented sight and movement.

It was useless to go on. He crouched where he lay, listening to the wind keening from the North and the now close and familiar sounds from below. The clank of a bucket, oddly muffled, the low of a cow as she was led to shelter, the yelp of a dog.

That gave him his clue. He barked, sharp and loud, calling to the dog below and Rex heard his companion and answered, a welcome barking that went on even after the farmer had shouted at him.

When Rex stopped for breath Moss barked again.

"Dammit, that's Moss out there," the farmer called to his wife, and he stood in the doorway, staring at the swirling flakes. "What's happened to Wyn, then?"

Mair Thomas could only stare at him, white-faced. The dog had never come home alone before, not since he was a pup. Wyn had trained him too well to have sent him off in punishment for disobedience. Nor would he send the animal home alone on a night like this.

"What can you do?" she asked Dai, almost whispering, fear taking away her voice.

The farmer was already huddled into his coat, dialling at the telephone that was the only link with neighbours too far to see or call on casually.

"Damme, the line's dead," he said, after futile jerkings at the receiver rest.

"You can't go out in this." Mair pushed her dark hair back with her hands, a gesture of extreme worry that Dai recognised. He halted at the door, and called.

"Moss, here Moss. Come then, good dog."

The dog barked, and, given the guidance of a voice, crawled over the ridge, slipping on ice that had formed on top of a trickle of water coming out of the spring.

"That's Moss," Dai said.

He stared out into the night. Gathering darkness had hidden the world. A tree, normally stark, was a blurred outline, soft with snow, fairylike by day, but now inimical, a symbol of the weather that paralysed all movement on the hill.

The dog barked again. It was dark, and he was too low to see the farmhouse lights, which, for him, were hidden behind the low wall that lay, humped and unrecognisable, blocking his view.

"Moss. Good lad, here then."

The voice was welcome, a warmth in the night. He plunged towards it and came to grief, with a yelp of fright, in the ditch, hidden and deep. He tried to claw his way out, but the soft snow was loose and fell away, leaving him beyond the wall, whimpering.

Dai Thomas brought the big torch that he used in the byre at calving time. It threw a feeble circle of light on the packed snow, beaten by the hooves of the cows into a flat and sodden mush that had thawed and frozen again until now it was glacierlike, threatening a man with sudden disaster if he failed to watch his step.

The dog whined again and Dai walked cautiously towards the sound, his voice reassuring.

He leaned over the wall, feeling it hard beneath the snow that gave beneath his weight, and saw the dog, a dark patch against the glitter. He moved, leaned down, gripped the loose scruff and heaved, and Moss, wild with pleasure at being once more with men, whined and wagged his tail and licked the man's hand in an ecstasy of welcome.

"Don't usually do that," Dai said, as he brought the dog into the warmth. He set food before it. Moss stared at him, whimpered and refused to eat.

"Well then, you'd best be eating. We can't find shepherd now," the man said, looking out into the darkness where the flakes swirled, feather light, drifting and clinging to byre and barn and stable. Beyond the patch of light one of the ponies yickered a complaint, afraid of the weather as snowflakes drifted in through his half open stable door.

Dai went out to shut it, sliding and cursing. He turned in time to see the dog, half a leg of lamb in its mouth, streak out into the night.

"Damned little thief," he said in fury. "Wouldn't touch his own food. Had to take mine."

"Are you going out on the hill?" Mair asked, busy at the sink.

Dai moved restlessly, looking out into the night. The snow came thickly, swirling towards him, eddying upwards as the wind blew, and he listened unhappily to the scream of the gale and the bluster in the chimney.

"Be two of us lost out there," he said at last, unwilling to face the truth, yet aware of his responsibility to his wife and the three lads safely asleep upstairs.

"First light," he said. "I'll get help from the Williams. Can't even track the dog in the snow. All tracks will be covered."

He was too restless for sleep. The thought of the shepherd irked him. Perhaps the man was dead, but more likely, buried in some drift, or fallen on the ice, to die by little inches in the wicked cold.

Long after his wife had gone upstairs he sat by the fire, watching the kittens play with a straw brought in from the yard on somebody's shoe, thinking of the wildness beyond the windows, and wishing that he had a warm job in town, not tied to the cattle and the bitter bleak hills, working for a pittance grubbed from the ground while other men fattened on the food he grew and played with their money, earned much more easily than his.

He forgot about Moss, and the stolen meat.

The dog was trying to retrace his path, back to the hill and the man that meant more to him than food and warmth. The meat held in his jaws made his mouth slaver, but he did not take a single bite. He picked his way carefully out of the farmyard, and back onto the hill.

The wind was behind him and in spite of the snow, the going was easier. A faint trace of scent lay on the ground, and he tracked back, with difficulty because the smell of mutton was strong in his nose, but it did not mask his own familiar trail, nor the rankness of the fox that caught a whiff of dog and meat and came running, only to find disaster as it met a drift that covered it completely and left it hungry and tantalised, buried until the thaw that found it thinner and wiser, not to be caught that way a second time.

The snow stopped. The moon broke through a layer of cloud, and shone on whiteness that covered all tracks, that hid the shepherd and the sheep that sheltered him, and hid the path.

Moss went on. In places he struggled, neck deep, dragging each leg from the snow, jumping and bounding on, more and more weary. Once he rested by a humped tree, and the meat tempted him badly, but he left it alone. It made his jaws ache, but he went on gamely.

He came to the patch where the shepherd lay, and stopped and looked in surprise at the unbroken snow. Carefully, he put the meat down, sniffed around and then began to dig. He found sheep and man in a hollow made by their breath, and the man, glad of fresh air, felt overwhelming disappointment when he saw the dog.

"Moss, Moss. You damned old fool. We'll both die out here now," he said, and the dog wagged a forlorn tail, unable to understand why he was not greeted with fervour.

He went back for the meat.

This time, he approached more cautiously, afraid of a cuff for his trouble. The shepherd, watching him with dull eyes, saw the half leg of lamb and stared at it, unbelieving.

"You durned old fool. You been back? I hope they saw you," he said, and reached out a hand to pat the wet coat. The dog dropped beside him, and licked his face. The sheep, too exhausted by snow and cold, were too apathetic to move. They watched Moss, eyes wary, but did not move. The lambing ewe struggled to bring her lamb to birth.

The shepherd took the meat. It was slimed and snowy, but he dragged at it with his teeth and spat the outer parts to the dog, who took his reward greedily, while the man gnawed at the bone, too hungry to care what he ate.

The farmer, tracking the dog through the snow two hours later, with the men from the farm in the hollow, found the pair of them asleep, the lamb cuddled between them, the ewe under the shepherd's head, acting as a pillow, her own head stretched to lick her son.

Dai Thomas stared at them, at the dog, which came to greet them, and at the bone that lay, gnawed clean, beside them.

"Moss brought me some dinner," the shepherd said, his eyes proud on the dog, as they dug the rock and snow away from his arm and helped him to stand, rolling him in blankets to go on the stretcher that the second farmer had provided. Hot coffee laced with rum quickly restored him, and the damage to his arm, apart from bruising, was not bad.

That night, bedded in the warm farmhouse on Mair

Thomas's settee, which she thought a better bed than his own above the cow byre until he was well and rested, Wyn watched his dog eat a meal fit for a king.

"Eh, Moss, you're a great lad," he said, and the dog turned and looked at him, and his tail beat a steady thunder on the hard floor before he returned to the dish that Mair had given him as his right.

ESCAPE

There was a watcher in the nearby tree. Man and dog and bird were unaware of him. Every instinct was focused on hunting. The peregrine flew high, circling, almost out of sight, while the setter searched the heather, and the man strode on, expectant.

The setter was quartering the ground, nose down, plumed tail waving. He was an English setter, thoroughbred and elegant, his lean, fit body covered in close curled fur that was patched and blotched with black and white and tan. His long ears drooped towards the ground, swinging as he ran. His plumed tail was eloquent.

Today was freedom, for man and bird and dog.

Sam Grant paused in his stride and turned his head, savouring the country. Forgotten, briefly, was his city desk, and the long sad tales that were the inevitable accompaniment of a busy criminal lawyer. Today he could forget his clients, and gain peace of mind from the wide horizons and the skill needed to deploy dog and bird together. He had trained them himself, and he had trained them well. He watched them with deepest satisfaction, valuing every unmarred and perfect moment.

He looked around him. Below him was a redbrick farmhouse, crouched against the ground, half hidden by shielding trees. Around it was farmland, freshly turned by the plough. Harvest had been early and the farmer was well ahead with his work. The rich dark earth was furrowed and clean.

The grassy headlands were contrast. Here long stems were weary with autumn tiredness, were a tangle of thin

94

yellow, stiff and wiry, foretelling winter greyness. One late poppy bloomed alone, blazing brightly, a spark of vivid colour among the drab herbage.

Sam turned away and looked over the moors. There was a crust of brown on the dulling heather, where seedpods succeeded the summer flowers. They spoke to him, not of death, but of life to come in the spring, and new brilliance. He breathed deeply and rubbed his hands together, his face glowing from exercise in the raw air.

The faraway lake was clear blue under a limpid sky. A lark spiralled, singing, saw the hawk and plunged downwards, its voice silenced. It hid under the trembling bushes, and the wind needled its soft brown feathers. Sam saw it plunge, and wished it well. Beyond the bushes were trees that blocked the horizon, their dry leaves turning to glowing gold, to slashing scarlet, to deep dull red, to rusty yellow and amber brown. Not a pestilence stricken multitude, but a vivid excitement, gladdening his eyes. Sam whistled softly, and walked on, wishing he could hold the scene in his mind for ever.

Autumn glowed on every bush; glowed in the bright haws; gleamed in the ditches where blackberries glistened juicily on the brambles that grew among the grasses; revealed itself in the soft grey lace tangle of Old Man's Beard, and the blue-black fruit that festooned the sloe bushes.

The air was fresh with the tang of frost, was clear as the silken surface of the lake, was winey and exciting. Sam grinned, and watched the dog. Markus was working through every clump, his busy nose analysing the scent on the ground, seeking for bird smell among the excitement of smells that lay on the moor. Rabbit smell and stoat smell; scent of weasel, tang of fox; rich mouth-watering rat stink, inciting him to find and kill. That was not why they were here. Markus knew that when the bird flew above him he was hunting winged game.

Sam looked upwards. The peregrine was flying freely, swinging on the wind. He needed exercise, and though the glove was ready and the lure to hand, Sam let him be. The bird spent the long weekdays clipped to the block in the garden, flying only briefly in the evenings, over the Common. Now he was free, and yet at the sweep and swing and call of the lure, he would return to the fist as if Sam had shouted his name. Tarquin!

Tarquin, King of the Wind and Lord of the Sky. Sam's vagrant fancy played around the bird, wishing he too could take wing, could sweep down the airstreams and plunge and soar. There was freedom.

Tarquin might have heard him, for in that moment he began to play, the sharp frosty air exciting him to display. He plunged downwards towards the dog, and Markus saw him and barked, knowing that no prey waited, that the bird was following a whim of its own, was teasing. The dog stopped his busy searching and ran towards the falcon.

Tarquin dived, and, only a few feet above the setter, braked and soared again, up into the sky, flying towards the yellow sun, light shining on his brown and white feathers, on the barred, strongly marked wings, and Sam forgot all desire to hunt and sat with his back against a tree, watching.

There was ecstasy in flight, in the effortless beat of arrowing wings, in the dive and swoop and soar and plunge, in the sharp braking and the sudden rising, in the spiralling upwards and straight falling downwards, in the breathtaking swiftness as the falcon thrust towards the sun.

Sam stretched himself and swung the lure. The bird was out of practice and would tire. The rook feathers circled his head, once twice, and a third time, and Tarquin dropped to snatch them, missed, and soared again. The lure swung slowly, and the falcon came in, and his sure talons gripped. He held the meat and flapped clumsily to the ground, no longer elegant, and mantled his wings above the food. Sam bent his glove, holding a piece of steak in his clenched fist.

The bird moved to the glove. The man folded the lure and stowed it away in his satchel, and caressed the sleek feathers with an ardent finger. The bird raised his head, staring, brilliant-eyed. He nibbled the finger gently with his beak and then tore delicately at the scrap of meat, holding it briefly and thoughtfully before he swallowed. The tiny bells on his jesses tinkled softly.

Tarquin!

Sam said the name over again, and the bird acknowledged it with a soft rousing of his feathers; with a lifting of his wings, and a quick settling, so that he was puffed to half his size again and brooding and magnificent.

Sam was filled with a sense of total achievement. When his hawk flew free, he could call it with the flash of feather on a string, with the swing and sweep and circle of the rook-wings, knowing the bird was tame, and would come to his master and come willingly, with love.

Tarquin!

The bird stepped delicately sideways and looked up, head alert, cocked to one side, bright eye pondering. Sam remembered the long days of manning his falcon, of taming his falcon. Days spent crooning to it softly to soothe and re-assure; days spent holding the bird every waking second; days spent gentling the bird when panic drove it to hang from his hand, jesses alone holding it firm, while its wings thrashed the air and fanned his face, as it experienced terror.

Terror from a passing car; from a running child; from a barking dog. Terror from a slamming door, from the sound of a vacuum cleaner; terror induced by household noise and by noise outside. Noises heard and never understood, but soon endured because Sam had reassured the bird, and shown it that there was no danger.

The slow days passed. Tarquin accepted Sam, fed from his fist, flew to his fist, asking for food, and then flew free, quartering the sky, soaring towards the sun, riding down the airstreams, spinning from the clouds and back to sanctuary, back to the hand of the man who fed him and gave him safe housing, and taught him not to fear the world.

Then came the training with the dog.

Now bird and dog worked together.

Sam stroked his bird again, and turned his head to seek his setter.

Markus was working. His busy nose was scenting the

ground, his expression that of total ecstasy. At times he paused, savouring delectation, eyes half closed, his expression that of a dedicated gourmet. He worked slowly, plumed tail signalling to his master. Sam watched, aware that the dog now had quarry in mind. He was working on a firm line. The man held the bird loosely, ready to slip the leash and let it fly. The bird, too, was watching the dog. Tarquin had long ago learned to interpret the signs Markus gave as he worked.

Markus had no thought beyond the scent on the ground. Lemony fragrant thyme, broken by his own heavy paws; bruised sharpness of clover; memory of fox, run past an hour since, the rank smells high where his pads had touched the ground; evocation of rat and shrew and weasel. And above all the signal he needed, the fresh clear call of a nearby partridge, flooding his nostrils, overriding all other smells, there in the heather beyond him. He ran forward, nose pointing, as he stared into the bushy clump.

Sam released the bird and heard the wingbeats as it spiralled upwards. His eyes too were on the heather, and on the dog, quivering with excitement from nose to very slowly moving tail, a faint tremor at the end of a body so still it might have been carved in marble. Only the dark nostrils showed life.

The partridge crouched, terrified, the smell of dog strong on the air. It was a young bird and inexperienced. There had been men shooting over the fields where he had fed with his covey. Too many birds had fallen to the sounding guns, and he had come for sanctuary to the moor. There had been an illusion of safety that the dog had shattered. The man moved forward; the dog barked, and the partridge flew, bolting for cover, not knowing where to find it. High above them the peregrine falcon sighted and plunged downwards, talons raked to kill.

He was too slow.

Throughout the morning there had been a keenly observant watcher. There was a sparrowhawk hidden in the hollow tree on the side of the hill. The bird had seen how the dog flushed game from the heather, had watched the peregrine waiting on, had seen it dive and kill once already that day. He had noted every movement and was ready.

He was a cunning bird, and had already weathered five summers and winters. He had hunted successfully for four broods of young, as well as his mate. He was sleek and well-fed, but he had not eaten that day and was hungry. He was always hungry. And the moor was not as well stocked as it had been even four years ago. He had to make shift where he could.

He hunted round the farm stacks, looking for rats and mice that fed in the straw and fed on the grain, and fed on stray eggs, laid adrift by wandering hens. He hunted too well for his own good, for twice he took the downling chicks, and the farmer raised his gun, protected bird or not. The sparrowhawk was wise and heeded the warning. He left the farm and kept to the high ground and the small birds hated him.

The peregrine was plunging, his speeding body tearing the air.

The sparrowhawk flew from the tree. He took the partridge cleanly, knocking it to the ground. It was too heavy for him to lift. He would have to eat where he stood. And he had not realised he would need to defend his prey.

The man shouted and the dog ran forward, barking angrily. The baulked peregrine circled and flew up, until he was only a dot high above them. The man stamped and waved his arms. The dog was a noisy frenzy, his barks echoing over the moors, deep angry bays that terrified the sparrowhawk.

Frustrated, he flew back to his perch in the tree.

The partridge lay on the ground, a tattered ragbag of feathers, flattened as an old mop. There was no sign of life. The dog sniffed and walked away, no longer interested. The man stooped to pick up the bird and add it to his game bag.

The partridge had not been killed. The sudden plunge had stunned it briefly and as it opened its eyes and saw the hawk above it, it feigned death, instantly, freezing against the ground, defending itself in the only way it knew against the rending beak and cruel talons.

The flight of the hawk gave it freedom, but man and dog were still there. If it stayed still perhaps they would go. There was no conscious thought in the bird's mind; only blind instinct, the learning of ages, that forced it to remain motionless.

The man reached out his hand.

The bird mustered its courage and flew up, hitting the huge red face that loomed above it, blundering over the heather to find fresh shelter under a hedge near the farmhouse and lie to recover its nerve.

Sam cursed, startled by the bird's thrusting flight. The dog barked again. Sam laughed, and whistled the dog. Let the bird be. It had earned another day of life. And he too had learned something fresh that day.

Jauntily, he swung the lure, once, and again, round his head until the peregrine flashed from the sky and seized the feathers and rode the rookwings to the ground. The dog sat on its haunches and watched, tongue lolling, breath panting, utterly content, so long as it was with its master.

The peregrine was enjoying flight. It left the lure and soared again, playing with the airstreams, teasing the man. Sam smiled. He had all day left to savour freedom. He swung the lure idly, not caring whether the bird came, or played for some minutes longer.

There was a shimmer in the wind as the bird swooped down the sky. There was the sound of rushing wings cutting the air. It took the lure with force and landed and mantled, and Sam held out his fist with food ready. He waited, watching each tearing bite, while the dog gnawed a meaty bone that he had brought with him. Beyond them, the sparrowhawk brooded, hungry.

When the bird had fed, Sam fastened it to the block in the rear of his station wagon, and took his own sandwiches and began to eat. He noted the sparrowhawk in the tree, and flung a lump of meat, bidding the dog to stay. The hawk swooped and was gone again, leaving only memory behind him.

The afternoon sun was a glow in the distant sky. Shadows sprawled from the trees across the ground. A pail clanked in the farmyard. Far away, a diesel train hooted as it entered a tunnel. A tractor engine hummed as the farmer drove down the narrow lane below them.

Sam savoured fresh bread and sliced beef, and chicken and ham. The falcon slept, tired by the morning's flying. The dog gnawed his bone.

The lark flew from the heather, spiralling ever higher, until its small body was a prick against the sun, and its soft call sounded merrily, leaving behind a memory that would never fade, of a day stolen from time, its perfection unmarred.

Sam stretched his legs and watched the sunshine play with the ripples on the distant lake. A small wind needled him. It was time to go.

They drove away, leaving the bone behind them.

The sparrowhawk took it as his trophy, and fed on the marrow left by the dog. The partridge slept, head under its wing, at the edge of the furrow, and, later, the moon brought an illusion of absolute peace to the moor.

A HOUND TO REMEMBER

They were litter brothers. Marksman and Mischief. They had played together from the day they first walked, tumbling asprawl, legs and tails inextricably mixed together, while the bitch watched them, her eyes proud.

They were the only sons in her first litter. She was a princess in her own right, and their sire was a king, his sons as valued as studs as he. This was the last litter the old boy would ever sire. The Huntsman hoped it would be the perfect litter. Champions all.

Their sire was Samson. There was no hound with a nose like Samson's. No hound with such strong legs, with such a well-made body, such a noble head. No other hound possessed such brilliant eyes, or one half of the old boy's sagacity. He had been at the forefront of the pack for most of his working life, but now it was time to retire. Time to lie by the fireside and dream of past glories. His day was done.

The Huntsman was sad. He felt as if he had lost a valuable ally. Samson could nose out the trail when every other hound had given up. Samson could call the pack after him, racing, nose down, after a fox they had lost an hour before. Samson led, all through his brilliant life. He was the Huntsman's favourite, all those years; first to greet him in the morning; first to come for food, defending his share against all the other hounds, very much master of the kennels. Now there was a new overlord, and the old boy no longer hunted. Time passed, all too soon.

No other hound was as brilliant as Samson. But these two showed great promise. The Huntsman felt the old eagerness as he watched them; the yearning to breed a champion of all time, a hound that would go down in legend. A hound to remember.

Samson had been a wonderful hound, but there was nothing outstanding in his career; only consistent memories for one man alone.

During the coming year, the Hunstman thought perhaps he had bred his champions of all time. Even the puppy walkers agreed that these two were exceptional. There was a special bond between them. They could not be separated or they pined. After three weeks apart, during which both failed to thrive, the Huntsman gave them best and put them on the same farm, where they settled down to puppy mischief, and to long days spent running wild in the huge fenced paddock where the ponies grazed.

It was a wonderful paddock. It was rank with wild flowers, and thick tussocky grass, and a thorny thicket ran right along one side of the wire fence, hiding many small creatures. The pups caught none of them, but the scent lay strong and hours could be spent chasing a tantalising smell, digging hopefully for some small beast that had long ago found sanctuary, while the floppy paws scattered the soft soil.

"Think they're moles, those two," the cowman said, grinning, as he watched the small busy sterns wagging furiously with excitement. He liked all creatures, and had an extra soft spot for the pups, often bringing a ball into the field to play football with them, helping them develop strong muscles that would serve them well when they came to work in earnest.

At the far end of the field was the horse pond, one end deep and clear, the other shallow and very muddy, the ground churned up by the heavy hooves. Here one day the pups found an old cloth, soaked in the stench of the pond bottom, rich and rewarding. They played with it till their lemon and white coats were patched with mud, and they stank of filth. When the farmwife came to call them in for supper she held her nose, and they paid dearly for the game.

Soap and water and the big tub were the worst experience of their brief lives. The children laughed as the pair tried to escape, running soapily round the barn, rolling in the dust and needing to be bathed again. When clean at last they ran riot, shaking water from their coats, soaking everyone in sight.

They learned fast. They learned about people, but most of all they learned about scent. There were smells all over the field. Taint of the old fox who came to steal the bones they had left, climbing up the fence as if there were no barrier at all. Scent of the big badger who came out of his sett in the corner, and drank from the pond. They spent hours nosing the ground, the hunting instinct so strong in them it could never be denied. They grew fast, and they grew fleet-footed.

In his spare time, the cowman amused himself by dragging a sack soaked in liver blood round the field, and then let them loose and watched them seek the track and discover a reward at the end of it. It was a wonderful game and the Huntsman thoroughly approved.

The cowman was young, without family cares, and he longed to work with the Hunt. At night his reading was of past Hunts, of great hounds and great Huntsmen. He wished he had lived in more leisurely days, when there were monied men about with time for the niceties of life. Here, they were always short handed and his spare time was scarce. The gaffer had even less.

The Huntsman took the pups back at the end of the year. They continued to show promise. He led the pack on a drag hunt, and watched how they worked. As always, they ran side by side, never faltering. They were among the leaders at the end of the day, and he went home singing under his breath. He had bred two champions.

By the time the pair were two years old he knew they were both winners. Both had sired pups. Both were in demand and both were winning prizes at the Shows. He had worked hard on their pedigree, eliminating all known faults, picking the dam with care. He had never needed to worry about Samson. The old boy was as near perfect as dammit.

Samson was now a house dog, too stiff for hunting. He hated his retirement. At the first note of the horn the old hound was at the window, his ardent stern wagging furiously, his eyes pleading.

He could not bear to be cooped indoors when there was a fox running on the hills.

One fine day he escaped from the confines of the house, and made his way out of the warm room, through the tiny garden and past the kennels and joined the milling pack, unnoticed at first.

He had no need today to stand at the window. His mouth dribbled in his eagerness to break out and run again, over the soft springy turf, with the wild excitement of fox-tang strong in his nostrils.

Today he could run with the fox in sight, an all pervading delectation, run till the fox was at bay and their work was done, and the pack was homeward bound again to the comfort of kennels and food and sleep and dreams in which they hunted endlessly and brought their quarry down.

Far away, beyond Low Meadow, came the clear sweet call, the sounding notes that summoned him to join the pack. He loped behind, going stiffly down the road, through the hole in the hawthorn hedge, across the sheep field, following the pack, slow and rheumaticky, but with the exercise easing the stiffness. He lifted his head and bayed. He was rejuvenated, was young and fit again, was strong and eager, and was hot on a scent that lay on the heather and spoke of joys to come. The Huntsman turned his head and saw the old hound. He could not send him home. He let him bide.

Over the field beyond Seven Sisters, running with his sons on either side of him. Samson often played with them, and there was a bond between the three. The Huntsman often wondered if Samson knew that these were his. Down the line of the ditch towards Long Nellie; up across the field under Windgather; over Castle Peak towards Longbottom; round the ruins that were said to be haunted, and through the Standing Stones, with the fox well ahead and the hounds running after, packed and solid, nose down on a red hot trail.

The fox was cunning and had run before. He was making

for the waterfall at Lathe Willows. There, he might slip
behind the fall and lose the hounds and run free, his feet
in water in one of the deep gullies, and make for the scree
behind it. Uphill and over the top and across the ford and
into new country. The hounds could not follow. The Huntsman noted the line of the run and frowned. There was
danger of losing the hounds. There were potholes on the
hill.

Over a grassy field and up the hill, veering westward, the
hounds behind and the foot followers with them. No country
for horses, this. Only the sturdy drab coated men, their
caps pulled forward, eyes intent, as they climbed the slopes,
watching the racing hounds and the running rascal that
had stolen twenty chickens, killing them in one single night,
adding insult to injury by burying them in the potato clamp
where the farmwife found them when she went to dig her
dinner. He was a rogue all right, that one.

The fox knew the ground well. He had been hunted three
times before, and was increasingly wily. He tracked back
through the ditch and up again over the Six Acre, past
Wiggery's farm at Dark Hollow, and over the Crest and
was off again, his tongue lolling. He was thirsty but he
dared not stop to drink.

Samson and his two sons were firm on the trail. The
ground favoured the old hound, for none could run fast
here. Game old boy, the Huntsman thought as he watched
the veteran plod along, his busy nose eager. A pity he
couldn't work with them still. Experience counted, here as
everywhere else. Samson brought back memories of other
days, when both of them were younger. Old bones ached,
whether dog or human, the Huntsman thought wryly,
favouring an aching knee. He watched the fox angle through
the heather, his back and brush showing in a rusty flash.

The sky was the colour of a bluetit's throat, and was
streaked with pearly cloud. The sun shone warm, driving
away the last traces of frost. A mist hovered over the low-
lying meadows in the valley but here the air was clear and
a man could breathe.

The fox reached the edge of the fall. He slipped behind

the raging water, and vanished. The hounds raced after. The Huntsman raised his horn to call them off.

He was too late.

Marksman slipped and lost his footing. He plunged into the fall, his body hurtling with the water, speeding downwards, any sound he might have made lost in the thunderous grumble of the surge. The other hounds backed away. The fox ran free. The Huntsman could do nothing. He collected the straggled pack and watched, his mouth grim. If only the hound fell clear.

The fox was forgotten. The Hunt spilled out, some of the men running to the pool beneath the fall. The other hounds returned to the horn's summons, but Mischief was hunting his brother. He had not seen him fall. He was bewildered by his sudden disappearance.

He lifted his head and bayed.

Samson ran to his son and nosed him. He had seen Marksman slip over the rock and he knew where he had gone. He nudged Mischief again, as if telling him to follow, and turned towards the steep scree.

The two of them, father and son, ran cautiously. The Huntsman watched in horror. One slip and the whole scree might slide in an avalanche and take both hounds with it. And threaten the pack. He called them back, noting the line that Samson was taking. The men watched, helpless, as the pair slithered on the loose shale, making for the pool below the waterfall.

It was a long pool, one side against the sheer cliff, the other difficult of access, except for one long spit that spread into the water. If the hound hit that, all would be over. It would have to be one of the best hounds he had ever bred, one of his favourites.

Marksman fell clear.

He was in the pool, at the far end, under the cliff, paddling water, not understanding what had happened to him. Down the scree, paw by careful paw, came his father and his brother. Samson set the pace, as if understanding the nature of the ground beneath him. He had worked on scree before, many years ago. He still remembered. The Huntsman held his breath. One slide could set the whole hillside rolling.

He called to the hound, but Marksman was deafened by the din of the water, was blinded by the falling spray, was bruised and shaken and had lost his senses. He paddled in a circle, whining, but no one heard his whimpers. He did not know which way to head. He trod water, working against the current, which was swinging him round. He could not see the rocky spit. And no one could reach him, not without swimming, and that was far too dangerous without a rope. One of the boys ran back to the nearest farm, but that was two miles away over rough country. And time was short. The hound was tiring.

A moment later, Samson jumped into the water.

The Huntsman cursed. The old hound hadn't a chance.

Samson swam to his son and nosed him, pushing him towards the spit where Mischief waited. The endless minutes passed. No one had eyes for anything but the two heads battling against the current, the old hound guiding the younger, showing him where to swim. And when they reached the spit, no one could help them. There was so little room. Two men volunteered to try and reach the rock, but the Huntsman would not let them risk their lives.

The hounds swam on, braving the tug and thrust of the current. The old hound was tiring. The water was icy.

Nobody spoke.

One man lit his pipe and stood watching, smoke wreathing his head. The pack milled, and the cowman held them in order. The Huntsman had forgotten them. He could not take his eyes off the two in the pool.

They reached the rock. Samson was behind Marksman, and pushed the younger hound. Mischief braced himself and seized his brother by the scruff. A minute later, the hound lay on the rock, panting, almost completely exhausted, while Mischief struggled to pull his father clear.

Samson made one tremendous effort and struggled out.

A few minutes later the three hounds skirted the narrow ledge and walked delicately towards the waiting men. The air was noisy with long pent breaths, released at last.

Scarves and shirts were given to dry the three soaked animals, and men worked willingly, delighted that the hounds were safe.

The Huntsman worked on Samson. The old hound was exhausted. He had saved his sons and returned to his master. His stern wagged feebly, and he licked the gnarled hand that tried to run him dry.

Five minutes later the Huntsman raised his horn.

Clear and thin and sorrowful, the notes echoed above the water, and the startled men listened, not to the Gone Away, but to the dying cadences of the Last Post. The old hound was dead.

The Huntsman carried him home. The pack followed.

They buried him where he could lie beneath the fox trails, in the path of the racing Hunt. And in later years, watching his sons grow to be even greater champions, the Huntsman often looked sadly at the small grave and thought of his hound's last day on the moor, and its ending.

Samson was indeed a hound to remember.

TWO AGAINST THE TWILIGHT

Old Davis leaned back against the Land Rover and looked down the field. It was the first time in weeks that he had a space to think—really think.

It had begun almost a year ago. The words of the newspaper he'd been holding had suddenly, inexplicably, blurred.

When it happened a week later, for the fifth time, he went to the doctor. And to the hospital. And to the hospital again.

They had been kind, very kind. They had sent him to Jonathan Ross, who had been blind since birth, and who taught Braille.

It did not prevent panic. Panic when the field of sheep first blurred into an indeterminate woolly mass. Panic when voices became more necessary for recognition than faces.

He had not told Boss yet. Maybe the sheep farmer wondered why the shepherd had suddenly taken to leashing the younger sheepdog, Moss, by his side. If so, he never said.

Moss had become Old Davis's lifeline. Instinctively the dog seemed to know what ailed his master. Today, walking up the lane towards the big field, in which the sheepdog trials were always held, the shepherd had misjudged the gate. The dog nudged his knee before he walked into the stone pillar beside it.

Old Davis managed to make a fair showing as he went through, head high, with the other sheepdog, Nell, behind him.

He did not need to see the scene clearly to know it. It

was dearly familiar, a part of his long years in the game.

The cars, the station wagons, the Land Rovers. They were parked side by side, all round the field, facing the huge arena, so that many of the visitors could sit in comfort rather than brave the wind that niggled across the grass.

There were forty competitors today. Each anxious to carry off the elaborately ornamental shepherd's crook— and the cup—that was the most coveted honour a man and his dog could win.

The dogs ranged the field. Old Davis knew every one of them, and could still, though dimly, recognise some of them.

All-white Ruff, a freak collie with a savage streak in him. That would be him snarling a warning at a visitor's dog.

Old Davis could just make the strange dog out, a curly white poodle flaunting a jaunty tail. He saw it as it brushed his legs.

Bess from Long Willows, a queen in her day, but growing old now, along with Mr. Jones, her owner. A little slow, but still a lovely bitch, black and white and gentle and able to single a lamb from the flock and bring it in seconds.

And that giant, curly-haired creature, sniffing at the Land Rover wheel beside him, and finally honouring it, was Dick Hasty's dog, Pat.

A powerful beast that never took his work seriously. Dear knew why Dick went on trying him. The dog was a fool. But then the younger men didn't know how to teach a beast.

Old Davis remembered hours spent with his dogs, training, perfecting, rewarding. He'd a way with them. He'd a line of wins behind him to prove it, and the championship title to defend.

He put his hand down to Nell, who had won last year, easily beating the clock, and on whom his hopes were pinned.

He couldn't do it next year. By then, the last remnants of his sight would have gone and nothing a soul could do about it.

But this year. . . . If only he could. . . .

He could barely see the sheep at the far end of the field now . . . only blurs of white, without definition. He'd have to rely on Nell.

If only she could do it. Bring off the hat trick, for this was the third year running. Then he could keep the trophy, the silver cup that stood on the judge's table, with his name on it twice.

Keep it to remember, to hold, to feel the shape under his hands. He would add the crook to those he treasured, using the best of them each year for the next event, to give him luck.

He held a handsome one now, its end intricately carved with acorns and oak leaves, and his name on it.

It was a good crook, too, easy to handle and well balanced. Made by Dai Price Richards and he was a master. Not many left.

Paddy Rourke was taking his turn now. Old Davis disapproved of Paddy. He had not even the decency to dress for the occasion. He had come, as he always did, in old grey flannels and a bright red jersey three sizes too large and with a hole in the arm.

Old Davis, and all the other shepherds and farmers, did proper respect to the occasion. They came in their Sunday suits, a mite tight and uncomfortable, but showing a proper spirit, and with brand-new caps.

Paddy whistled. He used a nose whistle, a tiny thing that fitted into his hand and, capped on his nose, sent a shrill note down the field, warning the dog of a need for action.

Old Davis thought it an affectation. Men had been given mouths and fingers. If they couldn't make the right noise with those, then Lord help them. They needed His help.

Paddy sent his dog, Lou, down the field right-handed. Old Davis could just see the speeding black back as the sheepdog streaked towards the four ewes.

They had been released at the far end of the field and were standing huddled for reassurance, lost and bewildered, needing guidance. Their tiny brains did not allow them to do a thing for themselves except flee from danger when deer, or running fox, or hurtling dog, came near.

Old Davis shook his head. The dog would lose time. Not only had Paddy sent him out the long way round, but he had omitted to study his ground.

There was a hummock, higher than a collie, blocking the dog's view. There was a line of trees to negotiate, and, furthermore, there was a cross wind, coming from the North-East. It would carry the scent of the sheep away from the dog.

Paddy's whistle was the only sound in the silent field. Men stood eagerly against the ropes, careful not to spoil the view from those in cars, commenting briefly on the skill of the man, or on his faults.

The dog had reached the sheep. He circled behind them, slowly, warily, legs half bent.

Paddy was signalling to him to go slow, slow, not to hurry or panic the sheep—keep them walking, lad, walking —that's the way then, good lad—over to me, over to me, come bye.

And just as the sheep were walking, puzzling but not alarmed, the dog crouching behind them, ears alert for the slightest signal, the white poodle frisked on to the field before his owners could stop him. He panicked the ewes so that they ran every which way, bleating in terror, as he leaped joyously at their heels.

The judge shouted. The poodle's owner appeared, apologetic, whistling and calling, but the animal would have none of it.

At last, Bob Fletcher, impatient at wasted time, gave his own collie the command, "see him off then." The dog chased the poodle out of the arena.

His owner caught him. Embarrassed and furious, railing at his wife, the man bundled the dog into the car and drove away.

"Good riddance," Old Davis thought.

Paddy was offered another chance, but knowing that his patience had gone, he shook his head.

"Number nine," the judge called.

Rod Nichols took his Sal out; Sal was Nell's rival, and her chief danger. If she'd improved . . .

Old Davis crouched and sat on the heavy steel bumper

of the Land Rover. Down here he could savour the field from a dog's height, and see where the wind was.

You had to think like a dog to handle one. On hot days, if you lay flat in the grass, and the grass was long and the air still, it was like a steamy jungle down there, close to the ground, out of the breeze.

The poor brute could be sweating his heart out for you.

So you drove him lightly, with frequent rests, high on a knoll where the wind cooled him, and let him drink.

Today, going up the field, he'd have the wind on his side. Then, crossing to the first gate, it would be in his face, a thing he'd hate, and an icy, bitter wind it was, too, low down.

Straight down the field to the pen, then it was clear going, and the wind behind him.

If only Nell could pull it off . . . his last triumph, something to savour, to remember, to talk about in the pub at night. At least he'd have conversation left.

Not to see the sheep—that would be hard. Especially the lambs, for each new-born was a personal triumph. He could ease a ewe at birth, or deliver a breech as cunningly as any vet. And savour his reward; the long-legged, jumping toy things, smudged and patched with black, tiny tails wagging deliriously as they drew life from the ewe.

Maybe Boss would still let him help. The dog would guide him. He could bring a lamb to birth, for that only needed skilful hands. No need for eyes. He could lift and carry them and give them bottles.

To be away from them—that would be unbearable. He had watched over them over sixty years now, from the day when, as a little lad, his father took him out, and began to teach him a lifetime's lore, such as you'd never find in books.

Sal was just finishing the course. This Old Davis could see. She was almost on top of him, shedding the sheep.

They had left the pen, the four bunched together, and now she must separate them in pairs. She was crouched, belly low on the ground, watching every movement.

"Seven and half minutes. Half a minute to complete," a voice, a stranger's, said behind Old Davis.

He watched. This was the tricky part, where many dogs failed.

Rod was circling behind the sheep, arms extended, the right one elongated by the crook which he held to stop them breaking away. They were manageable, this set.

Some of them were brutes. Bold, ready to challenge the dog, or almost, out of devilry it seemed, to play the fool and give him a run for his money, breaking wildly all over the field, with no chance to collect them again and drive them.

"Now."

Sal streaked between the four sheep, cutting them neatly into two pairs, one running right, away from the crook, the second pair off to the left, the bitch at their heels.

There was a burst of applause.

"Good lass, here to me."

She came running, stood for her reward, licking her master's face as he praised her.

Old Davis nodded. Always could tell when a man used his dog well. The dog repaid you, too.

"Good luck, Jo."

Rod was generous. He could afford to be. Sal, now herding the sheep into the far enclosure, had done him proud.

Old Davis and Rod had been friendly rivals over the last eight years. So far, Sal had never beaten Nell. Three years before, she'd taken the palm from his old Sue, who had died later that year, and been sincerely mourned by her master.

"Number ten. Jo Davis, from Wincey's End."

This was it.

As always, Old Davis found himself wondering about the odd name of the farm. It was rarely used, being more often referred to as Price-Evans, the Wincey's. Whether Wincey had been a man or not no one knew.

The thoughts made Old Davis aware that he was nervous. More so than ever before. His hands were wet with sweat and the crook was slippery. His tongue was dry. He had a film in front of his eyes and found it harder than usual to focus at all.

He frowned, screwing his eyes up, lifting his head blindly.

The farmer, from a few yards away, sighed, his suspicions confirmed. He watched as Old Davis spoke to Moss.

The dog led him to the side of the pen. Then, lead tucked into his collar, sat down and watched his master and Nell with eager eyes, as if knowing how much depended on this day.

"Now."

Old Davis could not see the sheep at the top of the field. They were skittish. One bounded absurdly and people laughed.

Nell had eyes only for him. He signalled her out left-handed, up the field along the little hollow that kept her out of the wind, so that she spied the sheep and dropped, without telling, behind them, stalking up like a cat, knowing she must not send them scampering.

This was the tricky bit, one part where he had to guess and pray Nell would do her job. Suddenly the answer came to him. She had done it before, so often, perhaps she could do it alone.

He sent urgent signals to her mentally, but nothing by voice or hand. Those watching who knew about dogs and men stared at each other, wondering if he was out of his mind.

Nell took the sheep down through the first gate, four in a straight row, never bunching them, never panicking them, never close enough for them to fear her.

Straight and true, then a right angle turn across the field with the wind teasing her and icy in her fur.

Moss pricked his ears and looked at his master. He should be telling Nell what to do. Instead he stood like a saint on a pillar, fierce, yet pathetic, staring towards his bitch as she trotted suddenly taking the sheep through the second gate and turning them to the pen.

Now he could see them.

Slowly, girl, slowly—gently, gently, my beauty, they're alarmed. There's something bothering them. Down girl, down.

Now, up again. No hurry.

It was hard to say, knowing the second hand of the speeding clock was ticking away, knowing that Sal had done it in record time, knowing that now, at this stage, anything could happen.

The sheep might miss the pen. A dog might run amok. Nell, over-eager, might drive them too fast and too far.

He held his breath, his only signal a soft whistle, given by mouth, not needing his fingers to augment the sound.

He had the pen gate open. Slowly, gently, not to panic the sheep. Nell, crouched low, her eyes bright, worked snakily behind them. Now!

She leaped, the sheep ran, and, in a second, were trapped before they knew, all four inside and the gate fast.

With a swift, smooth movement the dog was behind the pen, the gate was open and the four sheep outside again, heads turned puzzled. Why put them in and let them out so fast? they seemed to ask, looking from man to dog.

Now!

Nell leaped across; the deft crook parted the sheep; the two pairs were shed, so fast, so smoothly, it looked like magic and a roar went up from the crowd. A voice yelled: "Five and a half minutes by the clock. Did you ever see anything like that?"

Old Davis knew the cup was his, for ever. He called Nell. She felt his triumph and leaped at his face, licking, and leaped again, until Moss, jealous, came to his master.

"You old fool," Old Davis said, as he sent Nell off to pen the sheep.

She returned in double quick time, her tail wagging itself off.

"You've won, no doubt of that," Boss said, his voice rough with pride. "Nobody like you, Jo, with the dogs."

Now was the moment.

"I'll have to leave, though, Boss. I'm going blind. Doctor says so. Nothing can be done." It was worse than he feared.

The hand that gripped his was rough and fierce with reassurance.

"Think I'm letting the best shepherd I ever had, go? Be your age, Jo Davis. Teach the youngsters for me. We need your knowledge. With Moss to guide you and Nell to herd, there's always work for you."

That night, in the pub. holding his new crook and feeling the smooth metal of the cup beneath his proud hands, listening to the men laughing and joking with him, praising Nell, who lay at his feet, and Moss, who sat by his knee, ready to see for him, Old Davis knew the first peace he'd known for months.

And he knew something more, for unlike Jonathan Ross, who had been blind from birth, he would have visions.

Visions of sky and sun on the sea, and the long-legged smudgy lambs and the soft-fleeced sheep. And he had his hands.

He put one down now, to cold muzzle and warm tongue and silky fur, and he knew himself rich.

TRIGGER OF FATE

The bitch had been in labour for the greater part of the night. She was a half-breed, a cross between Alsatian and collie, and this was her first litter. She lay exhausted, but her eyes were content as she gazed at the small blind pups that nestled against her. She licked them, and sighed deeply. She was very thirsty, and she was hungry, but she was too tired to look for food. There was a plate in the corner of the shed.

Sunshine streamed through the dirty window. Beyond was an orchard, the trees old and gnarled and twisted, and uncared for. A dust of almond and cherry blossom drifted against the ground. A bird called near by, a clear, insistent repeated double note. Day had come, unnoticed.

The girl who slipped in through the doorway was small, and wore old and ugly clothes that fitted her badly. She was slender, almost as thin as the bitch, and her small face was tanned. She looked down now, from eyes that were large and a startling amber brown, contrasting with fine blonde hair and lashes so white that they were almost invisible. She bent to admire the pups, and a smile softened an expression that was far too grim for a child. She was no more than fourteen years old. Her hands were reddened and sore, but they lay gently on the dark head. The bitch growled softly, but also wagged her tail.

"I won't hurt them, silly," the girl said.

She wanted to lift the pups and hold them close, but she did not touch. They were so small, so vulnerable, blind, but intensely alive, their small bodies moving against one another, reaching out with incredibly tiny clawed feet towards the bitch's body, hungry mouths seeking constantly for the teats that would give them rich, life-giving milk.

The girl took meat, wrapped in paper, from her pocket. She had to smuggle it from her own plate. The gaffer would shoot this bitch if he found her. He hated all dogs, and he hated any creature that his stepdaughter loved. He had drowned her cat and killed her rabbit. He would drown the puppies. Lisa hated the gaffer. She never thought of her stepfather as anything else. She prayed, desperately, that one day he would drop dead. He was an ill man when sober. Drunk, he was a devil. And he was often drunk.

He must not know about the bitch. He never allowed her any pet of her own. She had long ago degenerated into maid of all work about the farm, working every second of her waking time when she was not at school. She helped with the cattle and the chickens and the pigs, cleaned the byres and styes, dragged the heavy churns. She loved all the small animals intensely, but never dared show her feelings. She longed for some creature of her own. Her mother was a shadow of a woman, subservient, afraid, always placating the man she wished she had never married. There were no other children. There was only Lisa, daughter of her first husband; fierce with hatred for her second, and never afraid to speak her mind, even if it ended, as it usually did, in trouble.

Lisa had found the bitch lying beneath the hedge, giving birth. Someone had abandoned her, not wanting the pups. The girl hated the unknown person too, and lifted the three pups that were already born and carried them to the old shed. The bitch followed. Now there were seven pups on the old sack beside her.

No one ever went to the orchard. Lisa had found the old shed one afternoon, soon after her mother married for the second time. She had escaped from the brooding anger that lay about the farm, and explored the no man's land at the end of their own ground. Her father had built a fine farm for a stranger to inherit. Lisa took the shed for her own, for sanctuary.

The floor was scrubbed and clean, as Lisa could not bear

dirt, but she had never touched the windows, lest anyone peep through and guess her secret. There was a shelf on which she kept a few old books bought, with treasured money, from the Vicarage bazaars at Christmas. Her stepfather thought reading a waste of time and an occupation for ninnies. He allowed no books in his house. Pernicious nonsense. Get on and do something useful.

Lisa bedded the bitch on clean sacking. She found an old bowl, and cleaned it and filled it with water. Food was a greater problem. The gaffer was mean with his money, needing everything that could be spared from the farm, and some that could not, for his own drinks. He was jovial in the Merry Man at night, treating everyone, buying the friendship he could not earn.

There was never anything left over for Lisa and her mother. Not even the egg money or the pig money was theirs. Lisa had so little pocket money that she could not even manage one tin of dog meat a week. And the bitch was starving. Her ribs protruded gauntly and her belly was tucked in in spite of the recent birth. If she had no milk, the pups would die.

Lisa took the bowl, that first day, and slipped into the field beside the orchard. She looked around her anxiously, lest there be any watching eyes. The gaffer was away, and her mother was busy in the house. They had no other help on the farm. Lisa knelt by old Daisy, who was nearest to the hedge and easiest to hand milk, and stripped one quarter of her udder. There would be more milk by milking time. She slipped back into the shed, and watched the bitch drink greedily. It was little enough, but it would have to suffice.

It was not enough. By morning the weakest pup was dead. Lisa buried the tiny body, before she went to school, tears spilling down her cheeks. She and the bitch were outcasts both. The other children laughed at the clothes her mother made her, cutting them down from her own, or from bargains bought from the Vicarage jumble sales. The gaffer considered clothes were to cover the body and keep it warm, and not an adornment. Lisa hated the good strong cloth and the ugly styles, and wished she went to a school where uniform was compulsory. But it was not. She lay on the floor after the burial, her arms round the bitch's neck. She had named her Shandy, because of the yellow glow in her coat. Shandy licked the girl's face, grateful for attention. Her life, too, had been hard.

That night, the bitch left her pups, and forced open the rickety door. The moon hung low in a midnight sky that was sullen with the promise of rain. There was a wind from the East that threatened the blossom. There was scent on the wood. Mouth watering, exciting, food scent. The bitch was starving and her pups needed milk and she was all mother instinct and fierce with the need to protect them and to provide for them. She was no longer tame. She was a wild thing, intent on killing.

There were rabbits in the field beyond the orchard. Shandy had smelled them the night before but had been too weak from giving birth. Now she was strong with mother-need, wanting food for her pups and determined to get it, no matter how.

She circled the field warily. Instinct told her to watch the wind. Instinct taught her things she had never known before. Instinct guided her to the final run, but as she pounced, she missed her kill. The rabbit scented her in that last second, and was away, bounding over the furrows, his bobtail flashing a panic signal that cleared the field. Thwarted, Shandy sat by the hedge, saliva streaming from her mouth.

The rabbits had not run far. The fox had been hunting too, and he was swifter than the bitch. He took the fattest rabbit and ran. Shandy scented fox tang. She saw the rabbit dangling from his jaws. She was desperate, and, behind her the pups were whimpering for milk, and she had no food inside her. She sprang, teeth vicious.

The startled fox dropped the rabbit. He fought back briefly, but was no match for mother hunger. He fled across the field, one ear hanging loose, his eye bleeding, his paw smarting.

Shandy fed, lying across the doorway of the hut, the moon spilling light over the pups that lay curled close, waiting for her. She was ready to defend them against any beast that might menace them.

When she had fed she buried the remains in the soft ground at the edge of the field, near the hut. It would serve for another meal. Sated at last, she cuddled the pups close and licked them clean. Now she had strength and cunning and she could hunt.

Visiting the little family in the shed on the ninth day after the birth, Lisa found that the biggest dog pup already had his eyes open. They stared up at her, unfocused, deep blue. She stroked him with a gentle finger, aware that he found the world unbelievably strange. He was so tiny, no bigger than one of the bitch's ears, yet he was obviously growing. He put his face up to his mother's, and she licked him avidly, her tongue reassurance, her warm body safety, her smell delight. His two brothers and his sisters pressed against him.

The bitch, too, was fatter. She now had strength to hunt, and every night since the fight with the fox she had caught a rabbit. Lisa worried, and counted the ducks and hens, but none were missing, and on the twelfth morning she found a rabbit paw that the bitch had brought for the pups to play with. Lisa relaxed. Shandy was clever.

Whenever she could, she came to watch the pups. She had never seen such small animals play before. Kittens on the farm were drowned and they had no dog. The gaffer was afraid of them, as they always hated him. Lisa was amused by the antics of the tiny fluffy animals that tumbled over one another and bit and growled and raged in mock battles.

The biggest pup was her favourite. He was bold, coming up to her, quite unafraid, snuggling against her when she held him, licking her face in a frenzy of affection. She had never known such love. It was lonely on the farm; so many years since her own father died. Her mother had changed. She had married the gaffer, who had been cowman in her father's day, thinking it the best thing to do. She had been wrong, but there was no going back. The farmhouse was filled with hate.

The pups thrived. Lisa laughed; it was years since she

had laughed at anything, but the little animals were so funny as they staggered on uncertain legs, unable to work out which to move first so that they fell in a roll of legs and tail. The biggest pup loved his tail. It eluded him and he tried to catch it, running in circles, striving to grab but it evaded him until he discovered he could lean it against Lisa's leg and snatch it, behaving as if it were some animal that had a mind of its own, rather than part of himself. Sometimes he stalked it, and barked in annoyance because it would not stay still and let him catch it.

When he did catch it he rolled on his back, mouth merry, and his eyes laughed up at Lisa. When his tail slipped out of his mouth he sucked his paw. Lisa was already beginning to think of him as her own. He was already a character, at four weeks old. If only she could keep him hidden. But how did you keep a dog hidden? It was not like a cat. There were three in the barn and the gaffer knew nothing of them. They kept out of his way. He allowed the two farm cats that he knew about. They caught rats. But he did not allow kittens.

He even shot the foal that was born when the mare jumped the fence and ran to the stallion three miles away. It needed feeding. And food cost money, and the gaffer's world was a carefully balanced one, budgeted to give him the maximum amount of money spare to treat his friends at night. Nothing was allowed to interfere with that. The farm was isolated. Lisa's mother could not drive and never left the farm. The gaffer did the shopping. Few people knew how his family lived.

Lisa came daily to see the pups whenever she could steal time. She made her way by devious routes, lest the gaffer spy on her. He would have no mercy. Moreover, he would be even more cruel if he knew that Lisa loved the pups. The girl reminded the man of her father, who had always been a man to obey, standing no nonsense. The gaffer grinned when he thought of him, long ago in his grave, unable to protest at the life his one-time wife and his daughter led. All those years of envy to be paid for, and pay they did. The woman was a daft fool, unable to stand up for herself, timid and useless. There were braver women in the village than she. And willing, too. The girl was different, but he'd break her yet.

There was no breaking. Lisa had her father's strength, and she defied her stepfather. She had a fierce love of living, of the beasts around her, of the fall and lie of the land, of the shape and colour of the trees, and of the house where she had been born. Nothing he could do could counteract that.

She loved the farmhouse, black and white timbers blending with the trees under which it sheltered, marrying with the land, built as if part of the landscape, as no modern home was ever built. There was a warmth about the place, in spite of the gaffer, that came from long ages of generous living.

And her mother still kept it proudly.

Inside the house the windows shone and the old oak furniture glowed in the firelight. The kitchen was snug, but it lacked the cats and the dog that had stretched on the hearthrug in her father's time. The gaffer brought them nothing but himself and the gun that was always present, leaning in the chimney corner. He loaded it each morning and went shooting in the fields. He cleaned it meticulously, lavishing on it the only care he knew. Sometimes Lisa looked at the gun with longing.

The gaffer was drinking more. He came home at night, stumbling down the drive, and threatened and bullied and shouted. The shed became a refuge. One night he was so unbearable that Lisa slipped out of bed, and took her blanket and curled on the sacks beside the bitch, with the comfort of the warm bodies round her and the pups curled gently against her, their small breaths faint on the air.

It was peaceful in the fields. Lisa looked through the open door. Moonglow silvered the grass. Moonlight etched the trees dark against the starry sky. Moongleam shimmered on the hedgerow flowers and on the fallen blossoms. Moon trails lay across the pups. Lisa reached for her favourite and cuddled him close against her. She slept.

The next week brought problems. The pups were becoming adventurous. They followed their mother to the door, and squealed to her to return. Lisa became constantly watchful, slipping away often, sure the gaffer would hear them, would find them, would kill them. And if he did, she would kill him.

The daunting thought terrified her. She had to keep them safe for her own sake. It was no use asking her mother's help. Her mother had retreated into a make-believe world of her own, not wishing to face reality. A world where life was normal and she cooked and cleaned, and pretended all was well.

There were still brief respites from fear, when Lisa watched the pups. They had found a length of rag in the shed, and learned to play tug with it, each one pulling furiously, growling at his litter mates, twisting and teasing, striving to get it for his own. The biggest pup was most frequent victor. He pulled valiantly, small body tensed, legs braced. Suddenly the whole rag was his and he ran off to play with it alone, shaking it, killing it, all by himself in the corner of the shed.

He snaked it in the dust, fascinated by the writhing shape. He rolled on his back and held it between his fore-paws and mouthed it. Lisa laughed softly. He was so endearing. He was so absurd.

One day, winning, he tired of the rag and took it outside. He would make it safe, and find it again when he wanted it. He began to dig. The flying earth fascinated him and he forgot the rag. He forgot everything except the hole he was making, where the ground was soft. The other pups stole up and took his trophy, but he went on digging, until at last he was exhausted and fell asleep beside the hole, one small leg trailing inside. Lisa lifted him gently and put him with the other pups on the sacking. She closed the door and tried to wedge it. Shandy couldn't hunt. She would have to bring food, somehow, and the pups would soon need to be weaned. She stole from the pigs, hoping no one would notice.

Now the pups cried out to greet her when she came and yelped when she went away. She had to plan, or they would be discovered.

The gaffer had noticed her long absences and wondered about them. He thought perhaps she was meeting some lad from the village. He was a curious man and he had to know. Also, he would step in and prevent any nonsense. When she slipped away after milking, carrying the bitch's water bowl, he was hidden in the barn, behind the door and out of sight.

He followed her, cautiously, taking care not to be seen.

When she had gone he went to the shed and saw the bitch and the pups. He would wait until she had gone to school. When she returned she would find seven dead bodies in the shed. Useless little slut. Stealing his food and his milk. No wonder the old cow's yield was down. Did she think she could cheat him?

But there was much to do that day and it was market day. He decided to wait until Lisa was asleep. She could make her find in the morning. He brooded angrily all day, his face lowering, as he watched six cows being sold, and took the money and counted it avidly.

He thought about the bitch, but first he would call in at the Merry Man and celebrate the good price he had made for the cattle .

Lisa spent the evening with the puppies. Her mother was no kind of company. Even in the evenings she cleaned the house, polishing endlessly and rarely spoke. There was nothing to say. It had all been said, long ago, and she and Lisa never agreed. And there was no getting the gaffer out. They were dependent on him for food and keep and he was there for ever.

It was very late that night when the gaffer came home. Lisa was asleep. He would be drunk and she was sure he did not know of the little family in the shed, so there was nothing to fear.

He came in, wild with drink and furious with anger at his stepdaughter's audacity in keeping the bitch and pups hidden, almost on his own land. The orchard marched with his biggest field. He hoped to buy it some day. The owner had died, and no one claimed the ground. The girl had defied him. She was a thief, and deceitful and she should suffer. He loaded the gun, his hands shaking, and went out into the night.

He stumbled into the starlit orchard. The moon was not yet risen. The sky was cloudless. The blossom was gone. The trees held the first small fruits of the season and a dry wind rustled the branches.

The bitch heard footsteps. They were unfamiliar footsteps and she sat, tensed. The shed door was wedged. The man dragged the wedge away and flung the door wide. He could see nothing. The shed was dark and no moon revealed the family, curled close in the corner, the bitch now standing above her young, a deep growl in her throat, her ruff bristling. She scented fear and she scented anger, and she had known both before.

Anger meant blows and meant kicks. Fear meant harsh voices and unpredictable humans. She had her pups to defend. She sprang.

Lisa heard the gunshot.

Terrified, she jumped out of bed. It had come from the orchard and there was only one man with a gun. She ran, not caring that the air was fresh and she was wearing nothing but an old nightdress, that had once belonged to someone far larger than she. There was no one there to see.

The gaffer lay where he had fallen. He had been carrying the gun carelessly, and he had not seen the bitch jump. Lisa went for help, although she knew that help would be too late.

The gaffer was buried, and her mother began to behave as if she was waking from a long nightmare. The house was freed of his brooding menace. On the night after the funeral Lisa went to the shed and picked up the pups and brought them, and the bitch, indoors. She walked through the wet grass, savouring relief from fear. There was not one atom of pity. The gaffer was gone and good riddance. Now they could live again.

The bitch walked into the kitchen fearfully. Lisa put the pups on the hearthrug and brought food and milk. The pups ran to their mother to suckle. The biggest pup came to Lisa. She lifted him, and held him close.

Her mother watched, saying nothing. When the bitch had fed, the woman took the plate and washed it. She found an old bowl , that had once belonged to Lisa's father's sheepdog, and filled it with water, and put it on the floor, in the old place, near the fender, where Shep's water had always stood.

She knelt beside the pups, touching them with gentle fingers. The bitch came, and licked the woman's face. Tears that had been repressed for years flooded her cheeks. Lisa made tea, and left her mother sitting in the wicker chair by the fire, with three puppies in her lap and the bitch and the rest of the family close against her.

The girl went out to the orchard, savouring the darkness. She picked a tiny apple, promise of fruit in the autumn, and she brought her books, and took them into the kitchen, and picked her favourite and began to read, softly, aloud, her face absorbed.

The years between were as if they had never been. Time went back to the days before the gaffer had marred their lives.

The bitch slept, unaware of the part she had played in bringing freedom.

Lisa named the biggest pup. She called him Nemesis.

A WELL-TRAINED DOG

I've always maintained that there is nothing in the world more rewarding than a well-trained dog. "All you need to do," I explained to my wife, Jenny, "is to be firm, be consistent, and expect the dog to obey, and he will. Make sure he knows who's boss. It's as easy as training children."

Our two small boys came screaming through the hall, looked into the kitchen, where we were enjoying a quiet cup of coffee, and screamed off again.

"Do they have to?" I asked.

"They're being burglar alarms," Jenny said.

A fusillade of "bang-bangs" echoed in my eardrums.

"Now they're being burglars."

My wife is brilliant at interpreting the child mind.

"Couldn't they be quiet burglars and quiet burglar alarms?" I suggested.

It wasn't even worth a reply.

I thought about that dog. I brooded about it. I had always wanted an animal in the house. Nothing was better for boys than a good, big dog to romp with, to take for walks, to care for.

I saw myself walking down the High Street, accompanied by a Saint Bernard, or perhaps a Great Dane. The boys walked beside me, the four of us causing heads to turn, and people to stare with admiring glances.

I began to read the advertisements in the Pets for Sale column.

It was surprising how rarely anyone had a pup on offer. I could buy budgerigars by the score, kittens of all varieties.

I could have a pony, "guaranteed quiet; 14 hands. Traffic trained."

I could buy an alligator.

The boys would love an alligator, especially if it lived in the bath and prevented them from using it. But I couldn't imagine Jenny being charmed with it. She hates spiders and daddy-long-legs make her scream, and even worms give her the creeps.

Night after night I scanned the column. Then I found my dog. "One year old, house trained, free to good home. Owner reluctant to part, but going abroad."

I was sure I had a good home. But I did not tell the family of my plans. If nothing came of them, nobody would be disappointed.

I went to the address.

The dog lived in a beautiful detached house, set well back from the road. Trees sheltered the grounds. (No one could call them a mere garden.) A gravelled drive led to an oak-studded front door.

I knocked, diffidently. My mini looked very small and lonely and out of place parked out there.

A woman with all the gloss of a fashion model, and the expensive clothes to match, opened the door.

"I've come to offer the dog a good home," I said, feeling both stupid and shabby.

Surely she didn't dress like that every day? Pearls and diamond brooch and all?

She led me into a room that would have swallowed the whole of my house. The dog followed us in.

It was a generously made dog, with large lolloping paws. I had never seen such a make before. It had a hint of Boxer, a tinge of Alsatian, a taint of Great Dane, a glimpse of Retriever.

"This is Lollo," she said.

It seemed a ridiculous name for a dog.

"Lollo. Good dog." I said.

Lollo looked at me with immense superciliousness and yawned, exhibiting enormous teeth and a cavernous maw.

I wondered if the boys would be thrilled. If the dog stood on its hind legs, it would dwarf them.

"I have been so worried," the lovely lady went on in a fluting voice. "Nobody else has answered the ad and we are flying out tomorrow.

"There is the basket, and here are the brushes, and these four plates belong to the dog. Come on, Lollo. On the lead."

The dog stood up, unfolding immense legs. Bemused, I took the lead. Events seemed to be happening faster than I expected.

"I know you'll be friends," Lollo's ex-owner said, and gave me a vague but captivating smile. She closed the door firmly.

Lollo looked at me and sat down, plainly sure that he was being kidnapped. I coaxed and soothed, and finally dragged him into the car. He filled the back seat.

The dog might have cost nothing, but I would obviously need a larger car to fit the family in as well.

I drove as far as the gate and heard ominous noises behind me. I turned my head. Lollo had been very sick.

Jenny met me at our gate.

"Dickie's cut his head and Johnny's fallen off the swing," she said, then looked at Lollo who was struggling out of the car. "Have you gone mad?"

It was not a propitious beginning.

"This is our dog," I said.

I avoided her eyes, which had the look in them that I knew so well.

She had developed it when I bought a dishwasher at an antique sale. It was a very good dishwasher, but we would have had to build an annex to house it.

At the next auction, it fetched five pounds less than I paid for it.

Jenny had developed that same look when I bought our first car. It was a beautiful car, a period piece, a genuine antique. Unluckily it seldom went farther than the end of the road, and Jenny wanted a car to drive the children to school.

Yes, I knew that look.

"His owners are going abroad and want a good home," I said. "The poor dog is missing them."

"The poor dog is a bitch, as any fool could see," Jenny said acidly. "You're old enough to know the difference. She is also about to whelp. I don't think she has room there. You'd better do something about it. And clean up that filthy mess. I'm not looking after a brute like that."

"She came from a stately home," I said lamely.

"I don't care if she came from Buckingham Palace. Anyway, they have the sense to have small dogs," Jenny answered, and marched away, her nose held as high as it would go.

I extricated Lollo and cleaned the car.

I took her into the kitchen, where she occupied all the floor space in front of the fire. She looked immensely unhappy, and so did Jenny.

"It's a most unhygienic-looking beast, and you don't know where it's been," she said. "You don't know what the boys will pick up. And it's probably got fleas."

"Not from a home like that," I said.

Jenny sniffed.

I brought Lollo a bowl of milk and she drank hungrily. I stroked her tentatively. She licked my hand.

"Good dog," I said.

She looked at me soulfully and leaned her head on my arm. I was kneeling beside her. She began to whimper.

"You'd better get the Vet. I'm not acting midwife to a strange dog—I mean bitch," Jenny observed, walking through the kitchen and out again with a jelly and three plates.

I was apparently not going to be fed either.

"And we haven't any food for her," she called. "Nursing mothers need a special diet. Her owners were clever weren't they? I should think she costs about four pounds a week to feed. You'd better get a part time job on top of your other one, and earn the money to keep her."

The door slammed. It opened again.

"On second thoughts you'd better resign yourself to housekeeping and I'll get a job. I'm not staying in the house alone with that monster."

The door slammed a second time. A cup fell off the draining board and smashed on the tiles.

Lollo whined again.

I went to telephone the Vet. He listened and sighed.

When I went back to the kitchen Lollo had eaten the corner of the rug and started on a chair leg.

"She must be teething," Jenny said caustically, coming back for the sugar bowl. "Try her with one of our best chairs. It will probably taste better."

I fetched Lollo's basket from the car. She climbed inside, and climbed out again and looked at me. There was not really room inside it to give birth to a mouse, let alone a pup or so.

Johnny put his head round the door.

"It's big," he said. He thought hard. "I don't like big dogs. I want a teensy weensy weensy weensy. . . ."

"OK, son, you've made your point," I said hurriedly.

Johnny can go on like that for days.

Dicky came into the kitchen and went out again. Howling.

"I don't like that dog," he sobbed, and I looked away when Jenny came into the kitchen again for the milk.

"Brute," she hissed.

I wasn't sure which of us she was referring to.

The Vet came. At midnight the Vet and I were still supervising delivery of the puppies. We had, by then, reached eight. By two o'clock we were exhausted, but Lollo was not. There were eleven.

By five in the morning the Vet thought the delivery was complete. He was wrong. The fifteenth pup made its way into the light, and moved its tiny claws and yawned.

"I congratulate you," the Vet said dryly. "You are now the proud owner of eight bitches and eight dogs. And you owe me twelve pounds for delivery fees.

"I'll send you a diet sheet. And she needs cod liver oil, and Bemax, and I should supplement her with one of the more nourishing milk producing foods. She's going to need a lot of milk. And meat. And at least two eggs and a pint of milk a day."

He left, yawning.

"Monday morning," he said, as he drove away.

I had forgotten. Jenny had no idea that we now had sixteen dogs in the house and I had to go to work. In just three and a half hours.

Lollo was lying with a bemused expression on her face. And small wonder. Not every dog . . . I mean bitch . . . has fifteen pups at one go.

I began to do sums.

Twelve pounds to the Vet. And meat bills, and a pint of milk and two eggs a day and all those vitamins.

I didn't know how to face Jenny.

She came into the kitchen at seven o'clock. I was asleep in the chair but her gasp woke me up.

"I hope you're pleased with yourself," she said. "Not everyone manages twelve dogs at one go."

"Sixteen," I said foolishly, and ducked just in time to avoid the dish-mop she threw at me.

Lollo, sensing the atmosphere, bayed, then, quite sure I was being wantonly attacked, growled.

"That does it," Jenny said, "That ferocious brute goes . . . now."

"I can't turn her out in that condition," I said. "Who on earth would want her?"

"The R.S.P.C.A. Or the Vet. Or advertise. We can't keep her. We need a bigger house. And a bigger car. Just for that."

Johnny crept into the kitchen.

"She had babies," he said, ecstatic. And put out a hand.

Lollo growled.

"Get rid of that dog . . . I mean bitch," Jenny shouted, grabbing Johnny and erupting from the kitchen.

She put her head round the door.

"I'm not speaking to you until you do."

It was time to go to work.

I looked at Lollo and she looked at me. I wished I had known what I was taking on when I answered that advertisement.

I thought of little else all day.

I made several mistakes in my calculations, and I gave

Mr. Jenson, who is one of the Bank's most important custo-
mers, ten pounds too little when he came to cash a
cheque.

All I could think of was Lollo, and Jenny there on her
own. I expected the telephone to ring all morning.

By afternoon I was expecting the police to call, to tell
me that my wife had been savaged by the bitch—or worse,
that Jenny was under arrest for cruelty to animals.

Nothing happened.

I arrived home to find the house peaceful. Lollo lay by
the fire with her puppies. The boys were watching her feed
them and making uninhibited remarks about the process.

Jenny looked smug.

"I've settled everything," she said.

She handed me the evening paper.

There, under Pets for Sale, was a notice.

"FOR SALE. Eight dog puppies and seven bitch puppies.
Unusual breed. £5 each, to good homes only."

"Jenny?" It was all I could find to say.

"I've sold all of them already," Jenny said smugly.

She began to laugh. "It's the first time any of your invest-
ments has shown a profit."

I looked at my wife, and she looked back at me, her
eyes bright with amusement.

"Oh, Peter, you are a fool," she said, and rubbed her
face against mine.

Lollo wagged her tail, approving.

I sat blissful, and repeated my words of a few nights
before.

"There is nothing in the world more rewarding than a
well-trained dog."

"You mean bitch," Jenny said, and began to laugh again.
"Especially if you train her to have puppies!"

Lollo has been a main prop of our finances for the past
few years. She has had fifteen puppies twice and never less
than eleven. Her pups are so intelligent and in such high
demand that we have raised the price to ten pounds, and
still sell every one.

I did well to maintain that a dog was rewarding.

THE ROUND UP

The whip cracked down, once, twice and again.

The dog yelped, a high pitched agonised yowl that stopped the shepherd in his tracks. He turned, and shouted.

The drover was a big man, sullen faced and heavy fisted. He was a bad man when sober, but now he was drunk, and venting his anger on the dog. It was a sheepdog, a gaunt animal, its black and white fur matted with dirt, but it had spirit.

When the whip ceased its vicious slash, the dog bared its fangs and snarled at the man. The man kicked.

James Hogg had been shepherd at Ettrick for long enough, and his name was well known. The poems of the Ettrick shepherd were to make him famous later, but now they were only an evening's amusement and the price of a drink in the local inn. He was famed for much more than his poetry; for his fairness, for his knowledge of sheep that made the Ettrick farmer well envied by those who employed less able help, and for his way with dogs. He could train the biggest fool of a sheepdog that anyone knew, and many men sent their beasts to him for handling, and for teaching.

Hogg looked at the dog. Its legs were covered in sores. The whip had marked its body on more than one occasion and there was a long festering wound near the tail. For all that, as it faced him, it had a bold eye, and he recognised the breeding. This was a treasure of a dog. He could see that, though it was cowed and filthy, held unwillingly at the end of a frayed rope. Jock McKay from Glasgow was an ill man to cross, but Hogg would never allow an animal to be mistreated in his presence. He strode forward.

The dog recognised a man that he could trust. He whimpered and pulled at the rope, sensing sympathy.

"I'll buy that dog," Hogg said.

The drover stared at him, sure the man was mad. The dog was not worth one single penny, dead or alive, but if the fool would pay there would be the price of more drink in his pocket, and the dog was a plague and a pest and he could get himself another to work the cattle tomorrow. He was sick of droving, sick of the filthy beds in the flea-ridden inns, sick of the road. One day he'd be rich, and have his own carriage. Drink fired his fancy. He flung the rope to the shepherd.

"Take the damn fool. He's an ungenerous brute and I hate him," he said, and took the half crown that Hogg offered him, now certain that the shepherd was mad.

Hogg took the dog with him that night when he went to report to his gaffer. It was the most unattractive animal the Ettrick farmer had ever seen. It had an air of breeding about it, but the stark ribs and long thin legs and festering sores looked horrible; and the creature was alive with lice and fleas.

"Take the brute away," he said in disgust. "No one but a fool would buy that dog. I thought ye had more sense."

Hogg said nothing. He had already owned the dog for three hours, and been struck by its intelligence. The eyes might be running and sore, but they were kind and wise; and once, as they passed a sheep, the dog turned his head and eyed it and it moved at once. It was a good dog. No ordinary beast, but a dog that would be memorable, a once in a lifetime dog, a companion and the grandest of sheepdogs.

He named him Sirrah. He took him home and bathed the matted sores; he dealt with the vermin; he fed him, apart from his own dogs, because Sirrah was ravenous. Food could only have come rarely, and sudden plenty might be harmful. The dog was given a bowl of oatmeal gruel, and a bed in the straw of the outhouse.

He picked up slowly. The other farmhands laughed, and called him Bony and Tinribs, Scragend, and Scrawny. Hogg heeded none of them. He was a small man, brown skinned and brown eyed, weathered from long days spent with the sheep, and he was a shepherd born as well as bred.

He loved his work; enjoyed the long hours on the hills, enjoyed herding and gathering, shearing and lambing. Most of all, he enjoyed lambing, and fostering the orphans, finding a bitch that would suckle an orphaned lamb, or taking the wee beast to the old cow that never cared what youngling fed from her.

He waged constant war on crow and eagle; on the running fox and the stoat and weasel that might attack a sickly youngster. And he trained his dogs. Trained them to herd, to answer to the whistle, revelling as he watched them slip and sidle and snake in the grass. Down then, good dog then, and the dog was anchored to the ground, stiller than the pheasant chick hiding under cover in the field when the hawk hung high, watching for movement.

He trained Sirrah.

Here was achievement. He had never known anything like it. And because the other men laughed, he kept his training quiet, only handling the dog when well away from human eyes. Sirrah learned fast. He followed Hogg like a shadow, never before having known a man he could trust.

No more kicks and no more beatings. No more starvation. There was food in plenty and the dog filled out, showing himself to be well grown, and well muscled, a tough little animal with astonishing endurance, covering anything up to sixty miles a day as he helped his master. No other man had fed him so well or treated him so kindly. Even then, one hundred years and more ago, the Ettrick shepherd was an exception. Dogs had little value, and were easily replaced. There were always new pups on the farms, and to spare.

Hogg knew that no other dog could round up the flock so quickly and neatly without need of nip or bite. No other dog could bring in a lost lamb, astray in the heather; no other dog could single a sheep so swiftly, separating it from the herd, spying the land around him, driving it by the shortest and easiest route to bring it in, eyeing it with that proud bright eye that made the sheep obey instantly.

Within the year, dog and man were inseparable. Within the year Sirrah had lost all his nicknames. No one could call him scrawny now. He was a handsome dog with a splendid glossy coat, sleek as a seal's back, and a shine and a knowledge in his eyes that made men turn and look at him twice, and made some offer for him far more money than his shepherd earned in two months of Sundays.

Sirrah was not for sale. Sirrah was the shadow at his master's heels, was the patient companion in the local inn where the men's clothes steamed at night and firelight flickered on the rafters and the oil lamps burned kindly and glowed and the ale passed as freely as the easy jests and laughter. Sirrah lay by the shepherd's heels and watched closely.

He knew which man to avoid and which would give him a bite of cake, or even a sip from his glass, laughing as the dog drank the heady beer. He knew when the cat came into the room. Ginger ignored the dogs, knowing he could leap to safety on the dresser, where firelight reflected on the willow-pattern plates, and the landlord kept the rosettes he won with his cattle at the local shows. They were fattened on leavings from the brewery, and the beery oats gave a gleam to their coats that had no equal, and gave their breath a tang that men recognised swiftly, and grinned knowing its source.

Before long, even in that wild country, men were talking about the Ettrick sheepdog as if it were some kind of wizard itself. It was bad country, rocky and mountainous, the grazing atrocious, the grass starveling poor. The wild sheep roamed where they chose. They strayed on the ledges and the lambs were always in trouble, leaping to the centre island of the little river, marooning themselves, afraid to jump back. The air was rent with the ewe's cries and Sirrah barked for help.

The dog learned the hills. He knew where the sheep hid in the winter storms. He knew where they sheltered from the gales; he knew where the lame ewe went to hide her lamb, and where the brown ewe preferred to graze, high in the corrie, alone, where lambing might prove dangerous, for she could be trapped and snowbound. He was eyes for his shepherd and ears for his shepherd and legs that ran endlessly, more willing than any lad.

Sirrah had a brain. He could work alone without any signal from his master. The other men were sure that dog and man could read each other's thoughts. When the brown ewe was caught by a sudden snowstorm the dog found her in a drift. He dug her free and herded her back to the rest of the flock, choosing the safe ways, knowing that she needed attention. Without him, she would have died.

Late one spring, when Sirrah was four years old, Hogg and the lad who helped him and was learning the trade collected the lambs from the hills. Seven hundred fine young beasts, ready for the sales, ready to put a fortune in the gaffer's pocket. Hogg eyed them with pleasure. They were clean fleeced, unlike their mothers, and moved in a packed mass, while Sirrah rounded them, cutting off any from retreat, keeping them in a single unit, a neat pattern that satisfied his eye and his instincts. Hogg whistled as he walked, and the lad chewed apples. He was still growing and always hungry.

It was a wild day. Snow brooded in the massy yellow clouds that sat on the high peaks, hiding them from the ground. Hogg pulled his coat more closely round him. He was not so young as he had been and rheumatism plagued him. Today his bones ached, and he was starting a cold. Thank God for Sirrah, who took all the hardship out of herding. Head down against the wind, they plodded on.

"We'll bed them in the hill fold," Hogg said, yelling the words, which were snatched from his mouth and blown away on the wind. The boy guessed his meaning and nodded. The lambs could be penned, and there was a stone hut where they could shelter for the night. They could build a fire to warm themselves. There was plenty of wood, and they could heat the broth he carried in a can. He blew on icy fingers, longing for rest and food.

The lambs were skittish, jumping and bumping, defying

the dog. Sirrah herded tirelessly. Hogg had long ceased to command his collie. The animal knew what to do without any need for words. Behind them the sky grew even darker. Wicked weather was brewing. Hogg had never seen anything like it. There was a green glow behind the yellow, and the wind's wail was a demon sound haunting from hell.

They waded in wet heather, man and boy concentrating on moving one numbed foot after the other. The thunder crash was a sudden shock, a terrifying clap of doom. The lambs broke in all directions, flying from total terror. The boom echoed through the mountains, a drum roll of fear.

Darkness dropped like a pall.

Snow flaked slowly, the flakes wet against chilled skin.

It was total disaster.

There was not a flicker of light in the overburdened sky. The lambs vanished as if they had never existed. Hogg stared at the boy who watched him, white faced. God alone knew what the gaffer would say. The whole of the spring lambing adrift on the mountain, at risk from ledge and gully and ravine, from snow and the icy slip on the rocky ridges. Sirrah was running, frantic, trying to round them. He had no chance.

He came back to his master, tail hanging low, and looked up at the man with pleading eyes.

There was only hopelessness in Hogg's voice.

"Sirrah," he said, looking down. "It's the end of the road for thee, and me, and the lad, for sure."

The dog wagged his tail uncertainly. The boy was shivering partly with cold and partly with fear. The Ettrick farmer was a just man, but this was beyond all reason. No shepherd had ever lost the whole of the lambing herd before. The gaffer's reactions were unimaginable.

"We couldna help it, lad," Hogg said, but it was poor comfort. They might, if lucky, make the hut. He whistled the dog.

Sirrah did not come.

He whistled again, and shouted, but the only answer was the echo of his voice and a wild wail from the wind that swept the hills.

The loss of the dog was as bad as the loss of the lambs. Hogg was miserably certain that Sirrah, afraid of punishment, had run off and would not return. There was nothing more to do.

Neither he nor the boy dared return to the farm. They spent a wet wild night, wading into bog and pool, without any light except that coming through ragged cloud from a few faint stars. They hunted the ground, seeking for the tracks of sheep, but there was no trace.

Seven hundred young spring lambs, the sole income of the farm until the shearing, had vanished like cloud on a hot summer day.

"God help us both if we dinna find them," Hogg said.

The boy said nothing.

Terror had dried up his mouth. The Ettrick farmer would be unbelievably angry. They plodded on, side by side, defeated. Worst of all, without the dog, there was little hope of rounding the flock in the morning. And Heaven alone knew where they were, running panic mad, pell mell in all directions. There was so much mountain and never a fence to contain them.

They dared not rest. They searched endlessly, using the faint starglim to help them, falling in bog and pool, hunting until tears of weariness and misery crept down the boy's cheeks. Hogg wondered if he even dared go back to his master when morning came. Perhaps it would be better to pack his belongings and leave home. But that was no solution.

There was not a sound of a single lamb. Not a trace of any sheep. The flock might have been a part of their imagination, and never real at all. And the hard flinty ground showed no tracks. Where the earth was a thin covering, there was also a shallow crust of snow. The boy was so tired he could barely move one numbed foot after another. Hogg blew on icy cold hands and felt sick.

"We'll hae to go back and confess," he said at last.

Dawn had come, miserably, out of the East. A cloud-streaked sky with snow promising later in the day, and a wan light that did nothing to raise their spirits. All round them, desolation. Nothing moved. The lambs must have bolted for miles.

Curlews wailed over the moors. A heron flapped slowly overhead on its way to a nearby tarn where the trout bred. Frogs hid in the rushes. The boy saw one jump into cover as the bird came into sight. The only other sound was the creak of the boots of the pair, as they squelched forlornly through the peat moss.

"Wait!" The boy was listening, his eyes suddenly bright. He grabbed Hogg's arm. "Listen."

They listened and stared at one another, unbelieving.

Sirrah had been busy.

He could see in the dark. He saw the lambs bolt for freedom and instinct overrode all other commands. Hogg could shout to his dog till the stars fell out of the Northern sky, but the dog would not listen. He had work to do.

He raced after the lambs. Night long, he chased them, he rounded them, and he drove the main body of the flock into a deep ravine. Here they milled senselessly, bereft of wits, none of them trying to move away. Round and round, round and round, while the dog ran out to find the stragglers, bringing one down from a little ledge that overhung the waterfall and dropped a hundred feet to a tumble of wickedly sharp boulders; chasing another across a narrow bridge, herding it safely, instinctively, back to its brothers; working the long night through, until, just before the dawn, he had every lamb penned, and not one missing.

He worked until the bleats died away, until there were no more forlorn noises from the mountain around him, until there was one huge satisfying mass of lambs down in the gully bottom.

Then he began to bark.

As Hogg and the boy listened, they heard the sound. The dog was exhausted, but still the barks went on, calling the shepherd to him, telling his master the lambs were safe, were here and please to come and rescue all of them.

"Sirrah!" Hogg exclaimed, and began to run, tiredness forgotten. As well as the barking, there was the sound of bleating sheep.

The boy followed.

The barking came from below them. The dog could not be seen, but they followed the sound and came at last to a deep gully. There at the bottom, almost too tired to bark, Sirrah lay. Beyond him, penned as neatly as if he had been working in familiar ground, were so many lambs that neither the shepherd nor the lad could believe their eyes.

The boy ran to the farm for another dog. Hogg clambered down the rocks. Sirrah was so tired that he had scarcely strength enough to wag his tail. He licked his master's hand. Hogg lifted the collie, who licked his master's face eagerly. The shepherd fed the dog the two sandwiches that he had been too miserable to eat the night before.

The boy returned with two men and two dogs. Together they counted the lambs. Not one missing. Not one harmed. Seven hundred of them penned, and all around them the ground was worn into a track, beaten by the feet of the dog, pounded out during the night as he circled the lambs endlessly, keeping the flock together, safe, for his master.

The other dogs took the lambs home. James Hogg, the Ettrick shepherd, walked after them, exhausted but light-hearted, his head held high, his dog held safely in his arms.

The drover's cur, the surly half-wild pup bought for a few pennies out of pity, had more than repaid his master. From that day he became a legend, and no other praise can be given today to a collie than to say "He's as fine a dog as Sirrah."

THE LESSON

"That damned collie!" roared old McClinton, up at the head of the sea loch, racing over bright orange-brown bladder wrack, flung by the tide, tripping and swearing, as Tammas took a duck from under his nose. One of the Khaki Campbells, and precious for next Christmas. The birds fared ill on the poor ground, and it was hard going to make ends glance at one another, here in the glum hills.

"That damned brute!" yelled Bess McKenzie, flinging a stone as Tammas barnstormed through her henyard and took a speckled matron that laid prime eggs and had handsome healthy chicks.

Dan threatened to shoot him, but Elspeth pleaded. She was town bred and pretty and young, and fretting for bright lights, not caring for the bleakness of the moors behind the croft, or the black peaty bog that lay in sulky pools reflecting orange stormlight from over the dour mountains that made men stare, bleak-eyed, at their sorry farms, and wish that scenery paid big dividends, and that the soil was black and rich and fruitful, proud to pour riches into their calloused hands that bled with the effort of coaxing life from the barrens.

"We'll be at odds with everyone if you cannot keep him home," Dan said helplessly, as the dog laid a blackcock at his feet. "He's been chasing sheep and chivvying deer, and there isn't a man on this side of the Black Hills that has a good word for us."

Tammas was a rogue. Plausible, handsome, even lovable, but, none the less, an incurable rascal. Or so Elspeth and Dan thought. He was beautiful, almost exotic, with his thick black and white coat, his immense fur ruff that stood up round his long muzzled head when he had been bathed, and eyes that were deep and secret and full of laughter.

Elspeth spoiled him. It was impossible to resist him, when he came to her, full of himself, plumed tail joyous, mouth a-gape, and laid his spoils at her feet.

Partridge. Chicken. Pheasant. Handsome grouse, and shining feathered duck.

"Tammas!" Her voice was reproach and for a moment his tail went down, his eyes shifted, looking at the day spilling over the cobbled yard, where their own chickens prowled enticingly, maddening him. He had not touched a bird on the farm since Dan had taught him with his own lead, doubled, and used as a whip.

But not even Dan could persuade him that poaching was wrong.

"That damned dog of the Meekings," the farmer at Corrie Beg said, as he saw the shining coated collie romp through his lambing ewes, and took his gun and his dog and a voice that made the hill thunder sound tame and domestic.

"He'll learn," Elspeth said, but learning, it appeared, was something that Tammas could not do.

He found trophies on the moors and in the deer forest, he chased sheep in the fields, and deer in the corries. He chased duck, and chased gulls, and did not even learn not to do that when a female, incensed by his proximity to her nest, dive bombed him and gashed the skin above his eye, leaving a jagged tear that scarred him, giving him a strangely mocking expression, as one eye seemed topped by a raised brow, quizzical.

He chased the cats and acquired a scarred nose and a torn ear. He fought any dog that challenged him.

"He's hopeless," Elspeth said, but she said it lovingly, as she might have done had he been a battle-marked small boy, and not a mere dog.

It was Hector McTigh who vowed to teach Tammas a lesson. Hector lived under the Black Brow, a threatening steep of rock that loomed over and dominated his small one-storey stone cottage, where the bare rooms were neat and scoured and shining.

It was said that Hector had been crossed in love long ago. He was a sour old man, his voice deep and sarcastic, his thick white beard bristling and assertive, his dark deep-set eyes ready to stare a man down and shame any woman that looked at him long enough.

Except Elspeth. She had moved into the next house, a scant half mile away, and knew that in the country it behoved a man to be neighbourly.

It startled Hector when he was first asked what ailed a limping sheep, but the mouth-watering scones that rewarded his diagnosis melted a corner of his heart that was hard as the Black Brow above him, and it flattered him to find that there was so much he could teach this young city couple, trying to make their way on a croft that was barer than the top mountain ridges, and as deep in heartbreak as the bleak windswept bog which was rumoured to hide a whole Highland regiment, bagpipers and all, in its sullen depths.

So that when Tammas came trespassing and chased a lambing ewe, Hector did not take his gun, but for the sake of little blonde Elspeth, who asked his advice, and brought him cakes and buns and scones from every baking, he determined to teach the dog a lesson.

Tammas knew him, and came tailwagging and unre-pentant, his long plume banner high, his mouth open and eager, and greeted Hector with fervour, as a man favoured with his mistress's friendship.

Hector put a plate of meat on the outhouse floor and locked the dog in, and went about his business.

He took the pony from the old field and put him in a smaller paddock, entirely surrounded by a high stone wall. The gate was open beneath, but Hector boarded it, making a barrier that would not let the dog escape. The pony, known in the village as "that black devil", grazed peaceably.

The old crofter left the pony and went for McTaggart. Mac was cropping in the far field. His temper was uncertain, and he hated dogs. He hated dogs more than he hated anything else in the whole wide world, and added to that, he was mean.

Mean natured and mean minded, with a vicious streak in him. For all that he was a splendid ram, and Hector's lambs were the finest in the area, the little males in high demand for future breeding stock, being hardy and immune to almost every ill that beset the hill sheep.

MacTaggart was roped and followed his master, glad of a change from solitude. He greeted Blackie with fervour. They were old friends and often together. He too began to graze.

The light was fading from the Western sky when Hector brought Tammas to the field. Tammas came eagerly, always anxious for new experiences, and with his mind on the grouse on the moor, a nice easy detour on his way home. His tail waved and his tongue lolled forward, and he walked, prick eared, eyes on the old man, wondering what new treat lay in store.

He was eased through the gate, and the exit was barred. Hector barricaded swiftly, and saw the dog stare at the pony and the ram and then shake himself eagerly. Tammas did not know which was most fun. Stampeding the moorland ponies that bolted with a thunder of hooves along the rocky paths, or leaping at the bleating silly sheep that fled from him in blind panic.

Old McTigh filled his crooked long-stemmed black pipe, and lit up, wreathing himself in smoke. He needed to watch. He did not doubt the outcome, but rescue might be necessary.

Tammas walked, stiff legged, towards the pony. The black beast raised his handsome head. His master groomed him with pride and the late sun picked out the sheen in his coat, picked out the gleam in his splendid mane, and picked out, too, the whites of his eyes as he rolled them, sighting on the dog.

He flattened his ears as Tammas ran in, ready to jump.

The pony reared, high on his hind legs, forelegs flailing the air. The dog had never seen such a sight and he dropped back, puzzled, onto his haunches and his own ears went down as the pony yickered in anger, turned as he landed, and jumped, all four hooves together, intent on trampling his enemy.

Tammas leaped backwards, almost rolling in his haste, and fled to the edge of the field, the pony after him, speeding over short tussocky grass, sliding once on a rocky outcrop that was flat as a table top, wheeling in fury, raging, bent on destroying the beast that intruded in his paddock.

The ram had been watching. As Tammas streaked past him he put his head down, and casually, without the slightest effort, took the dog on curved horns and tossed him to land, breathless and bewildered, a few feet away.

Tammas was brave. Nothing had ever outfaced him before, and he turned and faced the ram, growling deep in his throat. He barked, more to reassure himself than to threaten the prowling beast that was advancing towards him, head down, shoulders set, ready to fling him again. The bark turned to a snarl, and Tammas, realising that his enemy held an advantage, turned sideways, ready to jump in and harry the ram from the rear, but he was not fast enough.

Once more MacTaggart caught him and threw him and, before he had time to dodge, the pony thundered towards him, turned his back, and, lifting both hind legs beneath his tail, lashed out, catching the luckless dog between fore and hind legs, sending him spinning, over and over, to be fielded expertly on the ram's horns, and land, whimpering and crouching, beside the gate.

Hector leaned over and hauled the dog out as pony and ram turned to attack again.

"Have ye learned your lesson?" he asked.

Tammas whimpered. He was battered and bloody, cut over one eye, and bruised and aching. Hector led him through the far field, where the lambing ewes were gathered. The dog went meekly, almost afraid to look at them. He passed the chickens by without a second glance, afraid that they might turn traitor and attack him too, and Hector, to ram the lesson home, loosed the bantam cock from his cage, and watched as he descended, a minute and berserk fury, and sent Tammas scurrying for the sanctuary of the kitchen door, just ajar.

The dog crept inside, and Hector followed, to sniff at an enticing smell of new bread, and oatcakes, and scones, and curranty buns. Elspeth had been by, and left him some of the fruits of her baking. His mouth watered, and he took a bun, and, pitying the dog, crouched, panting on the rug, he threw him another, a rare piece of softness that he would never dream of acknowledging.

He bathed the cuts and put lotion on the bruises, and fastened a rope to the dog's collar, and took six new brown eggs, and walked up the hill to Elspeth and Dan.

"Tammas," Elspeth said in horror, as the battered warrior crept to her feet, tail low, and fawned, a thing he had never done before.

"Ah, weel, he's had a wee bit lesson, and I doot he'll not be chasing beasties any more," Hector said, and grinned suddenly behind his beard, for MacTaggart and the black pony had looked rarely funny, fighting mad, and the dog had put on a braver show than his own dog when it had had to be given such a lesson.

"What kind of lesson?" Elspeth wanted to know.

"Better not ask," Dan said, as the dog crawled to the hearthrug and stretched out to the fire, easing his aching bones.

Hector had no intention of telling. He shared a pot of tea, and to show he bore no ill-will, he gave a saucer of sugary thick tea to the dog, and Tammas, knowing he had met his match, rewarded him without malice, and licked the rough hand that patted his neck.

From that day, Tammas reformed, and kept to the house and yard, only venturing out when Dan or Elspeth invited him.

"I wish I knew what happened," Elspeth often said.

But Hector wasn't talking. Sufficient that he'd repaid a debt, even if the repayment was an odd one. Without, the dog would certainly have been shot by some irate farmer, before another year had passed.

Had Dan or Elspeth known more about dogs, Tammas could have told them, for he would not go near Hector's croft when MacTaggart or the black pony were anywhere about, and he skirted the sheep fields warily, never sure that the harmless ewes would not also turn and toss him unceremoniously.

"It must have been puppy mischief," Elspeth often said. Tammas merely wagged his tail and looked at her adoringly. He knew better. And what was more, he did not agree with Hector. It had been much more than a wee bit lesson. It had been a lesson he would never forget.

SUCH A GOOD DOG

He was SUCH a good dog, they told their friends and their relations and their neighbours. Absolutely no trouble at all. Of course, when he was at home, he did roll in the flower beds and bury his bones in the lawn, but he always stopped as soon as they told him. Well, almost as soon as they told him. He preferred them to catch hold of his collar and pull him off, as that was much more fun and he was a merry and playful little creature.

And they hardly saw him during the day. He was so good. He howled at the front door, as regular as the alarm clock each morning, at half past six, summer and winter alike, so that they could let him out. He might have had a clock inside him. And he was always home by seven for his evening meal, and after he had eaten it he was so quiet. He slept on the hearthrug in front of the fire, twitching in his dreams, placid and peaceful, the very essence of everything a dog should be.

Of course, he ought to be well trained as they had taken him to obedience class four times, so he knew exactly how to behave. At times, if he chose, he sat when they asked him, just to please them, his tail wagging furiously to show he knew how absurd they were, but he did live with them and he would obey, this time.

Immediately they released him he ran off to find a shoe or a slipper to chew. He liked handbags too, and chair legs, and there was something about his master's briefcase that always made him cock his leg. But he was such a good dog. No one could be cross with him. He was so apologetic when he had done wrong, coming with his ears back and his legs bent and his tail wagging in abject apology. He was so intelligent; he always knew.

He would go down, too, to order, when it suited him. Otherwise he woke and roamed the room restlessly, bringing a ball for them to throw, or putting a paw on a lap, or standing in front of the television set, effectively blocking the screen. Or curling on the settee, his nose on a visitor's lap, shedding hairs all over a smart suit, putting dirty paws on a clean blouse. No one could resist such friendly overtures, his family thought. He made all their guests so very welcome.

Sometimes he even came when he was called, although he never failed to come for food, so they kept his box of chocolates on the shelf with the cream biscuits that he liked so much, and a slab of cheese. He was passionately fond of cheese.

He was such a good dog and they loved him dearly.

They had bought him in a pet shop for two pounds, as a Christmas present for their younger son. Rog had always wanted a dog. He loved the puppy and carried it everywhere he went, lugging it lustily and being very gentle for a four year old. The pup was a lovable rascal, all fluff and pleading eyes and all of eight inches long. He was, the pet shop owner said, a pedigree poodle. He even had a pedigree to prove it. The man obligingly wrote it out for them while they waited. Champions all, his ancestors were.

Now the pup was four years old. The children had long ago lost interest in him. Rog found him a nuisance. There were far more interesting occupations than walking a dog. Besides, he could take care of himself. He went off on his own every day.

His name was Rap. A poodle might have had a hand in his ancestry, but there was a trace of Manchester terrier and more than a trace of Jack Russell; and somewhere, long ago, there had been a fell hound, and a collie, and perhaps retriever too, to account for the colour of his curly coat.

He was a golden brown dog with a long plumed tail and a stocky body; his head was long-muzzled, his ears half-pricked, half flopped, and he was the size of a largish wirehaired terrier. He had hunting instincts and ratting instincts, and a wicked sense of humour that showed itself in his merry eyes.

Over the years, he developed his own routine, and a number of entertainments. He loved the snow. He loved to dig, sending it up joyously behind him in a shower of cold clammy clods, but he only dug when women came walking near, dressed in furs, with nylon stockings. If he gauged his time right the snow shot up their skirts and they screamed in horror at the unexpected shock, while he sat and wagged a wicked tail and grinned with amused eyes. He had a sense of humour all right, and the children loved this game and encouraged it.

Most days were eventful for Rap, but one bright May morning was the day of his life. He woke early and howled to be let out, and was soon on his own, with a wonderful world to explore and the whole day to do it in, and no one at all to say No to him.

The day began well. He always chased the paper boy, feeling the familiar terrier thrill as he saw moving prey pass him. He raced after the bicycle, barking noisily. It was a new boy this morning. Tommy Parr had learned to land a kick on the barking nose, but Bobby Leigh was afraid of dogs and pedalled faster, to get away from the fierce little creature that was, he was sure, going to bite.

This was more fun that Tommy had been, and Rap increased his pace and began to jump up at the rapidly pedalling legs. Bobby was terrified, and turned too sharply at the end of the road. The bicycle hit the kerb, and Bobby fell, and lay still. Rap sniffed him, but the game had had an uninteresting end. Nothing moved to tempt him, and he ran off, while a motorist stopped his car to help the boy, who had cut his head, and was too dazed to stand up.

Rap ran on. The butcher at the end of the street was opening his shop. He always opened early, for the benefit of women who went out to work and could shop before the day began. He was whistling as he worked, cutting up the meat and throwing the bones for soup into a bucket under the bench. His knife needed sharpening and he went out to the back, to use his grindstone. It was all the dog had been waiting for. He raced into the shop, snatched a fillet of lamb from the bench and raced out.

The butcher was just in time to see the dog run out. He chased after him, shouting. Rap crossed the road. A car that was coming towards him braked sharply, skidded on a patch of oil, and hit a van driving in the opposite direction. Rap heard the crash and bolted, scared by the terrible noise. He raced down a narrow alley leaving chaos behind him.

There was a hole in the fence, and he crept through into a well kept garden, where he chewed the meat. Satisfied, he buried the remnants in a bed of bright tulips, destroying half the display. The owner ran at him, shouting, brandishing a broom. It wasn't the first time he had dug in her garden. If only she knew where he lived, but he never wore a collar, as the harsh leather chafed his neck and his owners thought it cruel.

He trotted back through the fence and into the alley. Across the gardens of the housing estate, stealing the food left for the birds, and chasing two cats, until he reached the little common. Here he slept for a while in the sun, curled under a thorn bush. One eye watched, and was rewarded when a woman brought a dog on a lead out for his midday walk.

Rap knew the dog of old. He was a gentle dog, and hated fighting. Rap ran in, snarling. The woman stamped and her dog crouched against her leg. Rap circled, militant, tail erect, dominant. He backed away, barking, and rushed in for one swift bite that made his antagonist yelp. Honour was satisfied. Rap had won the daily battle. He trotted off, leaving his defeated opponent with a torn ear that needed three stitches that afternoon.

Rap ran on. Over the new road, while tyres screamed and horns blared, crossing a ditch where the thick mud spattered his coat with a pungent delectable smell, and out to the fields. Here he lifted his head and sniffed. Here was all delight and his terrier blood was rampant. The heady sheep smell was all around him. The fields were full of new lambs and lambing ewes, and the farmers were busy.

Too busy.

Each field was only checked at the beginning and the end of the day.

Rap raced through the hedge, forcing a gap through which three lambs escaped that afternoon. The ewes ran from him, bleating wildly as he chased alongside them, leaping at their throats, his merry eyes mischievous. This was fun. This was exciting. One ewe was slow on her legs, half lame, and he jumped at her, and grabbed a mouthful of thick fleece in his jaws, savouring the taste. Terror lent her speed and she fled from him, running panic mad, until she dropped a dead lamb. Rap left her, as there was more interesting and livelier prey in sight.

The little lamb he saw was almost new. He had lived three days and two nights and had just learned to jump on his slender black legs. His tiny white face was black eared and smudged with black. His fleece was close curled, and he was as unreal as a child's toy, and as appealing. He ran, bleating, to his mother, who was resting, and butted her udder, his small tail wagging in frenzy.

He left her again, wanting to play. Rap raced at him. The lamb bolted, bleating. The ewe, enraged, chased after the dog. She butted him, and he rolled, but dodged her. By now the whole flock was milling, their terrified bleats deafening the air, so that the farmer heard and grabbed his gun, swearing. Damned dogs. Why must people let them wander?

Rap raced at the lamb again. His teeth met in the small throat, and tore. The lamb leaped out of the way. The farmer dared not fire. He might kill one of his sheep. The damned dog was in the middle of them. He ran at Rap, yelling.

The ewe charged. Rap was rolled head over tail and tail over head. He heard the angry shouts; he fled for the hole in the hedge and the speeding shot followed him, but missed. The farmer turned to the lamb. It was bleeding badly and in need of help and he had no time for the dog. Rap ran free.

He did not stop running until he was three fields away,

and the sounds behind him had died. Here he paused and sat, panting. He was thirsty, and went to drink from the ditch. He sat again, and scratched vigorously at a crawling tick, not yet embedded. He lifted his head.

There was news on the air.

There was a heady scent that drove everything else from his mind. He ran into the wind, in the direction from which it blew, crossing three fields and another road, crossing five gardens, until he came to the sixth, a big house on the edge of the common.

The scent was overpowering. It spoke of all delight. There were four other dogs waiting; a patched brown and white terrier, with a wise intelligent face and an arrogant stance, that growled a warning; a small black dog with raffish ears and a long plumed tail, that lay against the front door of the house, and challenged any dog that dared come near him; a tough golden labrador with a wrinkled muzzle and heavy shoulders and a lame leg; and a tiny long-haired chihuahua that belonged next door, and had slipped out unseen and was waiting as patiently as the rest, while inside the house a handsome Irish wolfhound bitch lay with her nose pressed wistfully against the french window and looked at her suitors.

At lunch time the bitch's owner came out to fetch the children home from school. She saw the waiting dogs. She went indoors. Two minutes later a bucket of water drenched Rap from nose to tail. His ardour considerably cooled, he shook himself vigorously and ran off. There would be no pleasure here. The bitch was too well guarded. Later, he might return. There was always hope, and Rap never took no for an answer. Plead long enough and ardently enough and the humans he belonged to always gave him his own way.

The sun was hot. Rap drowsed at the edge of a field, and dried his coat. Cattle had been here, but were now gone, and he rolled deliriously until his coat was patched with the greeny stain of cowpats and he smelled, to himself, ecstatic.

It was time to turn back. Soon the children would be home from school and there would be more fun. There were balls to chase, and sometimes catch and run off with, and chew, and leave lost in a wilderness of grass and bramble; there were more bicycles to chase; there were small girls who screamed when he played at jumping up and snapping. Rap liked an adventurous life. He trotted on, tail banner high, ears cocky, mouth a-gape, his whole expression that of total amusement.

The black and white cat had not seen him. The wind was wrong and carried no telltale smell; and the cat was fast asleep in a clump of new growing catmint, basking and comfortable. He did not wake until Rap nosed him.

He arched and spat and fled.

Rap chased him, barking, through the gardens, knocking over a small table on which a toddler was having his tea in the sunshine, leaving terrified wails behind him; over the road, where a boy had to brake suddenly to avoid dog and cat, through the legs of the pram-pushing mothers, homeward bound, chatting about the day's events and their children's progress; down the alley and through the fence and again through the tulip bed. This time, no one saw.

The cat saw a poplar tree, and sprang up the trunk, rising higher and higher, while Rap circled the bottom, barking. The cat reached the top and clung, terrified. Rap was soon bored and ran off. Later that evening the firemen rescued the cat, and were badly scratched for their trouble.

Rap rounded the corner. He stopped in the side road, his nose signalling. There was food near by. Wonderful food. Exciting food; mouth-watering food. He trotted in through the open gate.

The front door was also open as the owner of the house was fetching her child home from a neighbour's. Rap ran inside. A joint was cooling on the kitchen table, ready to be eaten later that day, as part of a salad supper.

Rap grabbed it and ran outside. No one saw him go, and the family cat went without her supper, as they thought that she was the culprit. Rap took his trophy home and fed under the blackcurrant bushes. Here he stayed until his mistress found him and bathed him and dried him.

It was not yet time to come indoors. There were tricycles to chase, and little girls with tempting fat running legs; he teased at a handkerchief and snatched it from a child who was blowing her nose, and took the ball from the boy at number nine, and made off with it, and dropped it, when he tired of it, down a hole in the road that workmen had dug that afternoon. He raced after Susan, the toddler at number two, and embraced her leg, holding it tightly, as he always did if he found her out of doors. She was playing with her older brother, and she screamed.

A passer-by drove Rap off, and he growled at the man who dared to challenge his right. The man looked for a collar, but there was nothing to show where he lived. Parents vowed vengeance and complained but no one could prove that Rap was the culprit. There were other dogs that looked like him. Many of them were his own pups.

Dusk came, nudging night. Street lamps shone and bright windows patched the gloom. There was a chill in the air and Rap thought of the warm fire, and the cosy house and the family waiting for him. It was time to go in. He barked at the door, and they opened it and he was home, with wagging tail and patting paw and the pleasure grin with which he greeted them.

His mistress had a visitor.

She called the dog. Rap had had a good day and was feeling compliant. He came at once, eager, and sat and begged, eyes wide and innocent, expression beguiling.

She patted his head and offered him a chocolate.

He took it politely and ate it delicately, savouring the taste.

"Say Thank You," she said, and obligingly, Rap barked.

"He's such a good dog," she said fondly, stroking the head that lay confidingly on her knee. "If only he wouldn't roll in muck. But you can't have everything. Dogs will be dogs. Really, he's no trouble at all. We never see him all day. We hardly know we have him."

She patted him again.

Rap wagged his tail and curled to sleep on the hearth-rug, stretched out, the warmth glowing on his belly. He dreamed he was chasing sheep again. He yapped with excitement and twitched his legs, and lived his day over again.

THE END